Where to Eat
HERTS, BUCKS & BEDS

THE INFORMATIVE GUIDE TO EATING OUT IN
THE COUNTIES OF HERTFORDSHIRE,
BUCKINGHAMSHIRE AND BEDFORDSHIRE

Editor: Jeff Evans
Art and Design: Lyndsey Blackburn, Sue Morgan
Editorial Assistant: Jackie Horne
Compilation: Margaret Whiteley

CONTENTS

Foreword	3
Tastes of Herts, Buc...	4
Ale and Hearty	9
Chef's Choice	10
Introduction	12
Where to Eat in Her...	13
Glossary	80
Index	84

Cover Photograph: The Bull Hotel, Gerrards Cross,
Buckinghamshire
Tastes of Herts, Bucks & Beds by Jackie Horne

Published by Kingsclere Publications Ltd.
Highfield House, 2 Highfield Avenue,
Newbury, Berkshire, RG14 5DS

Typeset by The LetterWorks, Reading, Berkshire
Produced through MRM Associates, Reading, Berkshire

Distributed in the UK by AA Publishing,
The Automobile Association,
Fanum House, Basingstoke, Hampshire, RG21 2EA

Extreme care is taken to ensure the accuracy of entries,
but neither the Editor nor the Publishers accept any liability
for errors, omissions or other mistakes, or any consequences arising therefrom.

Copyright © Kingsclere Publications Ltd. 1989. All rights reserved.

ISBN 0 86204 146 5

Foreword

Aidan McCormack

Foreword

BY AIDAN MCCORMACK

Hartwell House, situated in the beautiful Vale of Aylesbury, is the newest star on the Buckinghamshire horizon. We are in the heart of an area noted for its stately homes, charming villages and unspoilt countryside, all within easy reach of London, Oxford and Heathrow Airport, and a visit to Hartwell is like taking a step back into history; the dining room reflects the style of eminent Victorian architect John Soane and the library is haunted by the memories of the exiled Louis XVIII of France who used it as his salon.

I was very pleased to be asked to write the Foreword to this most informative guide and I hope you will keep it at hand or in the car and use it to explore our many culinary attractions. As you will see, the guide shows a wide selection of places in which to eat, with every taste and price range catered for.

With this guide you can't fail to find something to enjoy.

Aidan McCormack
Head Chef, Hartwell House, Aylesbury

Tastes of HERTS, BUCKS & BEDS

Mass produced, ready to cook meals and a proliferation of fast food chains and ethnic restaurants have blurred class distinctions that were once clearly defined by food. It is increasingly difficult to accept the old saying "Tell me what you eat and I'll tell you what you are". But up to the beginning of this century the foods a people ate were a direct reflection on their way of life and social standing. The foods of Herts, Bucks and Beds, the Northern Home Counties, reveal two distinct traits: a strong agricultural basis, in line with the other Midland shires, and a profitable market economy geared to supplying the ever-expanding London population. The former is particularly marked in Hertfordshire "that fine corn county" and the latter in Buckinghamshire, which developed a lucrative trade in fattening its ducks for city dinner tables, and Bedfordshire, with its market gardening.

In all three counties, farming was the backbone of the local economy and suet the staple of the daily diet; the suet providing sustenance to carry out the farming. Many of the region's specialities are based around the basic formula of lining a greased pudding basin with a paste of flour and suet, filling it with either meat, fish or fruit, wrapping it in a cloth and then boiling or steaming it for a couple of hours.

This method of cooking was very popular in the homes of ordinary cottagers whose only means of cooking was a heavy iron cauldron over the fire. Hertfordshire had rolled beef, a dish made with suet, herbs and stewing steak, whilst Buckinghamshire and Bedfordshire had their Clangers and Badgers. The Clanger was an ingenious meal in one, popular with agricultural workers for their midday lunch. It was made as a dumpling with meat at one end and fruit or jam at the other. Pork and apple was a popular combination because if one seeped into the other the taste would only be improved. The Badger was a

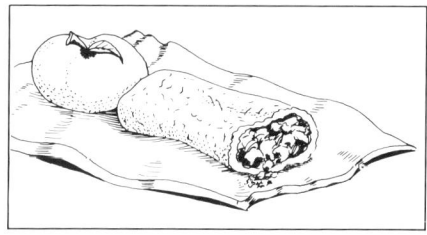

variation of this recipe; a dumpling

filled with bacon, sage, onion and raw potato. Crawley-bobs or freshwater crayfish were also rolled into dumplings. For a dessert dish there was Chiltern Hills' Puddings (made with tapioca, suet and raisins).

Villages in the past were self-contained communities often treading a thin line between poverty and subsistence and bound together by a mutual need to satisfy the most basic of human requirements for food, warmth and security. Life

followed the rhythm of the seasons and the feasts and festivities that were interwoven into its pattern were integral to the well-being of the community as a whole. Dependent upon the vagaries of nature, but seemingly helpless to control it, the ritualistic aspects of festivals offered protection and reassurance that the crop would be a bountiful one. They also provided a welcome release from the monotony of the daily grind, cementing the community together and underscoring its integration. The 20th century has witnessed a rigid separation between work and leisure with the result that the traditional festivals have lost their meaning, becoming warped by nostalgia and those who seek to profit from it. Today it is often difficult to imagine a way of life so deeply rooted in nature and which derived its only pleasure from celebrating or protecting the fruits of its labours. But it is the feasts and food customs, so closely tied to the farming year, which can provide us with a key to unlock the mysteries of life in former centuries.

January and February were bleak months of wintry weather and little food. It was a time for wassailing (to protect the cider orchards from evil spirits) and ploughing the fields. Even the religious festivities offered little relief since Lent, which begins mid-February, was a time of abstinence and denial. The three days preceding Lent, Collop Monday, Shrove Tuesday and Ash Wednesday, were all days of feasting before the long fast. On Collop Monday remaining bacon from the winter stores was eaten and any that was still left was cut into collops and hung until after Lent. Customs associated with Shrove Tuesday still thrive well into the

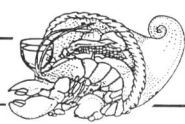

1980's; Olney yearly runs its pancake race down the High Street, whilst Baldock has a Doughnut Day when it is traditional to give children small cakes the size of a large nut, fried in lard. Ash Wednesday was fritters day.

The important religious events of Easter were also marked by food customs. Palm Sunday in the towns around St Albans was known as Fig Sunday, a reference to the fig tree that withered under Jesus's gaze as he entered Jerusalem. Many families would eat fig pudding for their Sunday lunch (a steamed pudding with suet, figs, flour, breadcrumbs

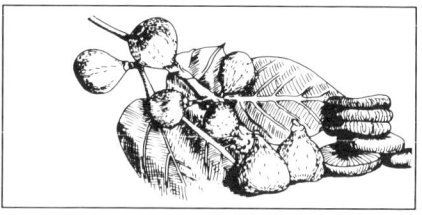

and eggs) and fig and apple jam for tea. Many of the religious customs that have become associated with Easter were adapted from earlier pagan origins until the two became indistinguishable. In earlier centuries, Easter was a time for the worship of Eostre, goddess of the spring, and spiced buns, signifying the sun, would be eaten to ward off evil spirits. These later evolved into hot cross buns, with those of St Albans much valued because it was said that if they were kept from one year to the next they would bring good luck. The buns were baked to a recipe handed down from the 14th century and were distributed to the poor at the Abbey. Indeed St Albans has a long tradition of providing for its poorer members. On New Year's Day, for example, Pope Ladies (spiced cakes in the shape of a lady) were distributed. This custom is thought to stem from the gratitude of a noble lady stranded near St Albans one night and given shelter by a nearby monastery. Easter Sunday lunch itself was traditionally one of lamb, which both symbolised the innocence of Christ and heralded the advent of spring.

Early spring, before the arrival of the first vegetables and meats of the season, was a particularly prosperous period for the population of Aylesbury. The town will always be synonymous with its prized ducks, pure white in colour and delicate in texture. Neither trait was acquired without a great deal of effort from

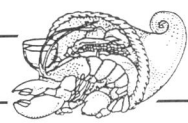

the duckers who reared them. In order to fatten the ducklings as quickly as possible, they were fed on a high protein diet, prevented from swimming, as this impeded their growth, and reared indoors to shield their skin from the sun. The result was that the ducks often had a better diet than the duckers and cluttered up already overcrowded cottages, sometimes sharing their masters' beds in order to keep warm. Slaughtering the ducks was complicated and had to be done in such a way that the blood would rush to the head. Plucking was then delayed so that blood would not start seeping through the pores. The advent of the railway during the 1830's was a great boon to the industry as the ducks could be quickly transported to the dinner tables of London, but from the late 19th century onwards the industry entered irreversible decline. This was initially the result of complacency but also weaknesses in the breed, from the constant inbreeding and later from crossbreeding with new breeds.

The midsummer months of the farming year were always fruitful ones. Whitsun usually marked the advent of warmer weather and was traditionally celebrated by eating veal with spring greens, followed by gooseberry tart. The highlight of the following month, June, was the

sheep shearing supper at which the local squire provided roast beef and plum pudding. June and July were both punctuated by a succession of rural festivities. At Hexton children rolled oranges down the hillsides, at Codicote there was a contest to climb a greasy pole for a leg of pork, Hertford and Royston had cattle fairs, Frithsden had a cherry fair and Ashwell had a village feast on 6th July. The first Sunday in July was widely known as Gooseberry Pie Sunday, although in the Chilterns, noted for its cherry orchards, Cherry Bounces (a black cherry pasty) were eaten.

The farming year reached its peak in late summer with the annual harvest, and the supper which followed was often celebrated as the major social event of the year, more so even than Christmas. Rabbits which had fattened themselves on the stubble fields were popular among the dishes served. Olney had a rabbit pudding with macaroni, onion and grated cheese and Bucks, a layered pie of rabbit, bacon and

7

chopped mushrooms. Hiring and mop fairs were also common at this time of year as all the service contracts were ending. At Bedford Warden Pears (baked pears) were eaten and Baldock had a cheese and onion fair. Many of these fairs coincided with Michaelmas when goose was the traditional dish and innkeepers would provide free ale and plum cake.

With the approach of winter, the carefree festivities of the summer months gave way to customs with more ritualistic overtones, such as on All Hallows Eve when the spirits of the dead arose. Young girls would also try and predict their future husbands by throwing nuts onto the fire. If the nut burst it was a good sign, but if it was left untouched by the heat it signified that the girl would remain an old maid. Customs such as these were reassuring and often buffered villagers against the harshness of winter. Its onset was dealt with more practically by the slaughter of a family's livestock, traditionally on November 11th, the day of Martinmas. Cured meat would sustain the family during the long months ahead and could also be sold. Bucks ham is often said to be the finest in the country because of its special nutty flavour which comes from the pigs feeding on the beech mast of the Chilterns.

Herts, Bucks and Beds were, therefore, very much the agricultural heartlands of the prosperous counties encircling London. Today this rural heritage is still very clear in many areas but it has been tempered by the commuter suburbs of London and the encroachment of light industry. However, vestiges of the past remain rooted in the present through the numerous craft exhibitions to be found in all three counties. Biggleswade in Bedfordshire is the setting of Holme Mill, once owned by the Jordan family of cereal bar fame and now open to the public, whilst south of Luton at Stockwood Park is a craft museum with working demonstrations. The counties' culinary traditions are characteristic of a solid yeoman diet and it is through them that we can recapture and bring to life a broader sense of the past, its atmosphere and the day to day working of its life.

Ale and Hearty

Ask any foreign visitor what he or she associates with England and amongst the answers you are sure to find "the English country inn". This magnificent institution is unique to this country and the envy of the world, its origins lying in Roman times and its colour bestowed by centuries of hospitality, close association with agricultural practices and the advent and demise of coaching. In the Northern Home Counties this heritage lives on and indeed has been nurtured in recent years; many atmospheric hostelries abound, not just in the country but in the town too, and with them thrive quality ales and beers.

In the late 1960's and early 1970's, this tradition was in jeopardy. Small brewers were being squeezed out of the market place by the big nationals and much of the local brewing heritage was being threatened. Fortunately, several of the area's independents survived, their traditional brews lasting with them. One of the most prominent was Charles Wells of Bedford, which not only lived to celebrate its centenary in 1976 but opened a bigger, more modern brewery to cater for the increased demand for its products. Today it serves an estate of 300 pubs, stretching from Lincolnshire to London and boasts an award-winning range of beers. Eagle is the traditional bitter, taking its name from the company logo, but most renowned is the premium cask beer Bombardier (named after Bombardier Billy Wells, the man who beat the gong at the start of Rank films).

Look out also for Hertfordshire brewers McMullen, established in 1827 and serving ale in over 150 pubs throughout the area, Banks and Taylor, set up in 1982 in Shefford, Bedfordshire, and Greene King, the East Anglian brewery, with around 800 pubs in the east of England.

Chef's Choice

*In each of our regional **Where to Eat** guides we ask an experienced chef, well-respected in the area to provide one of his favourite menus:*

Peter Chandler

Peter Chandler is chef-proprietor of Paris House Restaurant, Woburn. He enjoys the distinction of having been the Roux brothers' first English apprentice and trained with them at Le Gavroche in London and at The Waterside Inn, Bray in Berkshire. Now his own restaurant is recipient of many culinary accolades. Here he reveals a personal selection of dishes.

STARTER
Monkfish with Noodles
Monkfish has always been a favourite fish of mine because of its lovely meaty texture. Furthermore, it is so easy and versatile to combine with sauces or to pan-fry and serve slightly plainer.

WINE
Meursault Bernard Movey 1978
A fully matured, honey-flavoured dry Meursault. Excellent quality.

MAIN COURSE
Boeuf Bourguignon
What could get the taste buds tingling more than a classic boeuf à la bourguignonne. It is one of my all-time favourite country dishes and its rich, unctuous sauce and a garnish of vegetable make this a must.

WINE
Mercurey Rouge 1985
This is an underrated region, often passed over for its better-known companions, yet delicious.

DESSERT
Brandy Snap Tulips with Strawberries and Ice Cream
Texture, crispness, ice cream and fresh strawberries – what a combination! The perfect finish to a meal.

WINE
Château Coutet 1982
A Barsac wine of great quality and depth, with, for a dessert wine, deceptive dryness lingering on the palate.

Introduction

This *Where to Eat* guide has been compiled to offer readers a good cross-section of eating places in the area. We do not only concentrate on the most expensive or the 'most highly rated' but endeavour to provide details of establishments which cater for all tastes, styles, budgets and occasions. Readers may discover restaurants (formal and informal), pubs, wine bars, coffee shops and tearooms and we thank proprietors and managers for providing the factual information.

We do not intend to compete with the established 'gourmet guides'. *Where to Eat* gives the facts — opening hours and average prices — combined with a brief description of the establishment. We do not use symbols or ratings. *Where to Eat* simply sets the scene and allows you to make the choice.

We state whether an establishment is open for lunch or dinner and prices quoted are for an à la carte three course meal or a table d'hôte menu, including service, as well as an indication of the lowest priced wine. However, whilst we believe these details are correct, it is suggested that readers check, when making a reservation, that prices and other facts quoted meet their requirements.

Two indexes are included at the back of the guide so that readers can easily pinpoint an establishment or a town or village. We always advise readers to use these indexes as, occasionally, late changes can result in establishments not appearing in a strictly logical sequence.

We hope that *Where to Eat* will provide you with the basis for many intimate dinners, special family occasions, successful business lunches or, perhaps, just an informal snack. A mention of this guide when you book may prove worthwhile. Let us know how things turned out. We are always pleased to hear from readers, be it praise, recommendations or criticism. Mark your envelopes for the attention of 'The Editor, Where to Eat Series'. Our address is:
Kingsclere Publications Ltd.
Highfield House, 2 Highfield Avenue,
Newbury, Berkshire, RG14 5DS.

We look forward to hearing from you. Don't forget, *Where to Eat* guides are now available for nearly every region of Britain, Ireland and the Channel Islands, each freshly researched and revised every year. If you're planning a holiday contact us for the relevant guide. Details are to be found within this book.

Where to Eat
HERTS, BUCKS & BEDS

ST MICHAEL'S MANOR HOTEL
Fishpool Street, St Albans.
Tel: (0727) 64444

Hours: *Open for lunch and dinner (last orders 9.30pm).*
Average Prices: *A la Carte £20; Table d'Hôte £16; Sun lunch £14.*
Wines: *House wine £7.25 per bottle.*

Standing on ancient abbey lands, St Michael's Manor dates back in the main part to the 16th century. The manor is built with a combination of brick and stucco and has a particularly elegant Victorian glass conservatory overlooking the grounds to the rear. Here, five acres of lawns and specimen trees are crowned by a lake, all adding to the manor's peaceful atmosphere. Masses of fresh flowers continue the effect within. The Newling-Wards have been running the hotel for the last 24 years and have established a strong local reputation for their consistently high standards. In the dining room there is a choice of both table d'hôte and à la carte menus. The latter is expansive in its description of each dish, carefully prepared by chef Steve Juett. Begin with lobster bisque (lobster laced with fine cognac and double cream, served with scallops of lobster and Italian breadsticks), followed by cranberry magret (fanned breast of duck with a coulis of cranberries and blackcurrants), or fillet of lamb (with a lightly creamed green apple and cinnamon coulis). For dessert try some baked Alaska (Drambuie soaked sponge with layers of ice cream and meringue, baked in the oven).

Hertfordshire

JADE GARDEN

16-24 Spencer Street, St Albans.
Tel: (0727) 56077/62635
Hours: Open for lunch and dinner (last orders 11.30pm).
Average Prices: A la Carte £14; Table d'Hôte £8.50; banquets £13.50.
Wines: House wine £7.30 per bottle.

The speciality of The Jade Garden are lavish banquet meals of the kind that are traditional in China itself but which are not often seen in this country. The restaurant provides a nine course Cantonese banquet for 8-12 people. The combinations change regularly but a recent menu began with the Jade Garden special combination of chicken Phoenix, barbecued spare ribs and spring rolls, followed by chicken with sweetcorn in egg drop soup. Moving on to the main course there was lemon chicken, quick-fried prawns, fried whole fish with sweet and sour sauce, braised duck, stir-fried meats of three kinds (shredded chicken, pork and duck) and fried minced pork and prawn slices with greens. All dishes were served with fried rice and to conclude there were fruit fritters in syrup, followed by tea or coffee. Other dishes to be found on the regular à la carte selection included chicken with black beans and peppers, and steamed fresh sea bass with black bean sauce. Booking in advance is required for the banquet meals.

16-24 Spencer Street, St. Albans. Tel: 0727 56077/62635

Hertfordshire

LA PROVINCE RESTAURANT

	13 George Street, St Albans. Tel: (0727) 52142
Hours:	Open for lunch and dinner (last orders 9.45pm).
Average Prices:	A la Carte £16-£20; Sun lunch £9 (adults), £4.50 (children). New Pasta and Wine Restaurant from £6.50, lunch and evening, Mon-Fri.
Wines:	House wine £6.50 per bottle.

St Albans was one of the most important cities of the British Roman Empire and today its colourful history is reflected in the many buildings of note scattered throughout the town. La Province is situated in a 17th century building, still crowned by its original beams. A small bar greets diners at the entrance to both the main restaurant, which seats 30, and the conference/party room upstairs, also seating 30. The atmosphere is relaxed with music to soothe the ear and fresh flowers to please the eye. Cooking is French with, for example, crevettes de Nino (king prawns cooked in fresh herbs with garlic and wine), followed by magret de canard kumquats (duck breast cooked in red wine and brandy with an apricot and cream sauce). Desserts from the sweet trolley, or a selection from the French cheeseboard, conclude, whilst the wine list, covering 30 labels, leans towards France in its choice. Outside is a patio garden, overlooking the city's Medieval cathedral which was built on the site of the first Christian martyrdom and is today the oldest monastic church in use in all of Europe.

LA PROVINCE RESTAURANT

13 George Street, St. Albans
Telephone (0727) 52142

Hertfordshire

CLAUDIUS ITALIAN RESTAURANT

116 London Road, St Albans. Tel: (0727) 50527
Hours: Open for lunch and dinner. Closed Sun.
Average Prices: A la Carte £13; wine £5.50 per bottle.

The enthusiasm and dedication of Nello and Jennifer Orza shine through the cookery and atmosphere of their Claudius Restaurant. They serve a wide-ranging menu which offers pasta, fish and meat dishes such as sogliola Claudius (sole with smoked salmon in cream, with asparagus), bistecca Pompei (entrecôte in a tomato, cream and prawn sauce), filetto Cesare Augusto (steak with Dolcelatte, cream and port) and pollo Messalina (chicken with Mozzarella, prosciutto and almonds, in mandarin sauce). Home made desserts.

116 London Road
St Albans
Telephone: St Albans 50527 & 62428

SOPWELL HOUSE

Cottonmill Lane, Sopwell, St Albans.
Tel: (0727) 64477
Hours: Open for coffee, lunch, tea and dinner (last orders 9.30pm, 10pm Fri, 10.30pm Sat).
Average Prices: A la Carte £18.50; Table d'Hôte £14.50; snacks from £1.75.
Wines: House wine £7.50 per bottle.

Built during the 18th century for the Earls of Verulam and owned by the Mountbattens earlier this century, Sopwell House stands testament to the grace and elegance of Georgian country houses. Nature is strikingly displayed within the house by mature magnolias growing through the roof of what is now the restaurant. The room has a peach and pastel blue décor with wall stencilling and a large terrace for al fresco drinks and meals. The style of cooking is contemporary British with, for example as starters, Loch Fyne Scottish oak smoked salmon or forest mushrooms stuffed with Stilton. For a main course dish try breast of chicken with a quintet of peppercorns, served in a pastry case with salad, or fillet of beef Sopwell with a layer of parfait and claret and beef marrow sauce. To conclude there are desserts such as toffee ice cream with brandy. The house wine is Georges de Boeuf. For a lighter snack try the sandwiches and salad platters from the bar.

Hertfordshire

THE GOLDEN LION
London Colney, St Albans. Tel: (0727) 26596
Hours: Open for lunch and dinner (last orders 10pm). Bar meals.
Average Prices: A la Carte £7; Sun lunch £7; snacks from 95p.

London Colney stands just off junction 22 of the M25. The Golden Lion itself is very much a family pub with a large garden and a selection of burgers and jumbo sausages for the kids. The aim is to provide reasonably priced bar favourites such as roast chicken with sage and onion stuffing, batter-crisp scampi and ploughman's lunches. Real ales from the bar.

The Golden Lion
High Street, London Colney
St. Albans. Tel: (0727) 26596

HARPENDEN MOAT HOUSE HOTEL
Southdown Road, Harpenden. Tel: (058 27) 64111
Hours: Open for lunch and dinner (last orders 10pm).
Lounge snacks lunchtimes, except Sun.
Average Prices: A la Carte £23; lunch/Sun lunch £12.50; dinner £16; snacks from £2.
Wines: House wine £8.50 per bottle.

The Harpenden Moat House is located just off the A1081 overlooking Harpenden's East Common. This 300-year-old building has been very successfully converted into a four star hotel, maintaining many features from the Georgian period. Through the reception and lounge areas is the popular Cocktail Bar which stocks a wide range of spirits and liqueurs. The Cocktail Bar Manager, Vincenzo Catalano, has over 30 years' experience and has won awards for his exciting and exotic range of cocktails. Reflecting the quiet elegance of the Georgian era, the restaurant, which overlooks the gardens, features a ceiling painted in the Italian Renaissance style. The impressive décor is matched by care and expertise in both the quality and preparation of the cuisine and the professional polished service, given by Restaurant Manager Giuseppe Pasquale and his team. The à la carte selection prepared by head chef Neville Pease is extensive: the starters include Stilton and leek timbale, set on a bed of apple and port wine sauce; for a main course try perhaps fillet of beef served with a light mousse of chicken, encircled with chive butter sauce, and, for a sweet, a dark chocolate terrine with vanilla sauce.

17

Hertfordshire

QUEEN ADELAIDE PUBLIC HOUSE

120 London Road, Shenley. Tel: (0923) 856234
Hours: Open for coffee and lunch. Closed Sun. Bar meals.
Average Prices: Snacks £1.50-£3; house wine £3.50 per bottle.

Built in 1924 on the site of the Queen Adelaide Hall, this friendly pub serves wholesome pub cooking every lunchtime, except Sunday. Organic meats come from the local butcher and ham on the bone is a popular dish, as is the steak and kidney pie offered on Fridays. Vegetarian meals always available. Flowers and Whethereds real ales on draught. Regular live 60's music. Facilities for disabled visitors.

Queen Adelaide
Public House
120 London Road, Shenley, Radlett
Tel: Radlett (0923) 856234

THE COMET HOTEL

301 St Albans Road West, Hatfield. Tel: (070 72) 65411
Hours: Open for coffee, lunch and dinner.
Average Prices: A la Carte £17; Table d'Hôte £9.95; snacks from £1.25

The Comet Hotel was built during the 1930's to honour the expansion of the local aircraft industry and from the air its shape is of a 1934 Comet racer. There are two thematic restaurants: the Mosquito Grill and The De Havilland Restaurant. The latter has both a carvery and an à la carte choice that ranges from scampi de Havilland to tournedos of beef forestière. Vegetarian dishes too and a traditional Sunday lunch.

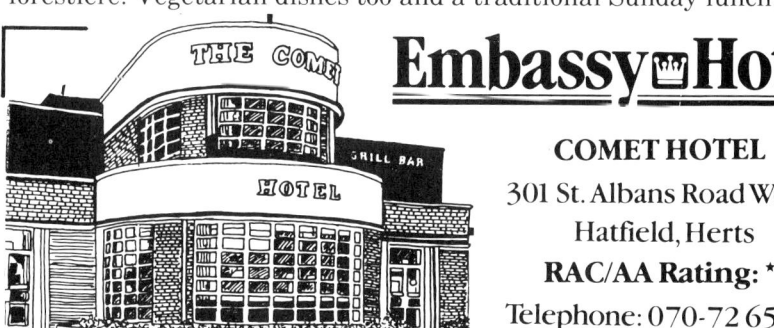

Embassy♛Hotels

COMET HOTEL
301 St. Albans Road West,
Hatfield, Herts
RAC/AA Rating: ***
Telephone: 070-72 65411.

THE EDGWAREBURY HOTEL

	Barnet Lane, Elstree. Tel: (01) 953 8227
Hours:	Open for coffee, lunch and dinner (last orders 10pm). Closed Sat lunch/Sun evening.
Average Prices:	A la Carte £17.50; Table d'Hôte £15.95; Sun lunch £14.50; bar lunch £9.50.
Wines:	House wine £6.95 per bottle.

The Edgwarebury Hotel is situated close to central London, but ten acres of grounds give it a secluded country atmosphere. Once a millionaire's mansion, then an exclusive country club and today an hotel, it has an elegant facade reflecting its past and characterized by a criss-cross of black and white timbering. Inside there is heavy oak beaming and intricate wood carvings in the public rooms, whilst the dining room is panelled and has a heavy stone fireplace. The menu has recently been changed with the arrival of a new chef and is traditionally British in style. Starters include a prawn and crab medley, or crab au gratin, followed by main course dishes such as loin of lamb enclosed in a pastry case and veal in a green pepper sauce. Desserts are all freshly-made and from a trolley. Try the Scottish cranachan (raspberries blended with cream and Drambuie). There are children's and vegetarian meals too. The hotel has also recently opened a 35 bedroomed extension to complement its conference facilities.

Hertfordshire

WEST LODGE PARK

Cockfosters Road, Hadley Wood, near Barnet.
Tel: (01) 440 8311
Hours: Open for coffee, lunch and dinner (last orders 9.30pm, 10pm Fri/Sat).
Average Prices: A la Carte £15. House wine £7.75 per bottle.

Enfield Chase is the setting for West Lodge Park. A lime tree avenue leads up to the house which is surrounded by 34 acres of grounds that range from formal gardens to a lake and famous arboretum. Inside, the atmosphere is very much that of a country seat with numerous antique portraits, dating mainly from the Stuart era and showing the various families connected with the house. The restaurant, run by Zacharias Komodromos, overlooks the gardens and has a terrace for summer drinks. The à la carte menu is changed monthly and prepared by head chef Jonathan Binns who has an international background having worked in Europe, the Middle East and on the Canberra. His style is based on traditional classical cuisine and influenced by modern French methods. Some recent specialities have included smoked salmon and spinach roulade with watercress sauce and forest mushrooms, baked in pastry with a rosemary sauce for starters, followed by medallions of venison stuffed with an apricot and herb filling and chanterelle sauce, and brochette of scampi and scallops with a saffron sauce, served with wild rice.

Cockfosters Rd.,
Hadley Wood,
Nr. Barnet,
Herts.
Tel: 01-440 8311

Hertfordshire

ROBIN HOOD PUBLIC HOUSE AND RESTAURANT
Ridgeway, Botany Bay, near Enfield. Tel: (01) 363 3781
Hours: Open for coffee, lunch and dinner (last orders 9.30pm). Bar meals.
Average Prices: A la Carte £12-£14; Sun lunch £9.50; snacks £1.30.
Wines: House wine £6 per litre.

Despite a setting on the outer limits of London, close to the M25, the countryside around the Robin Hood is open and very popular with walkers. The pub itself is ivy clad with the occasional peacock wandering through its garden, which has won London in Bloom awards. Flowers also add freshness and life to the dining room which offers traditional home-cooked fare. There is a selection of ten starters, ranging from chicken livers in a sherry sauce with rice or garlic bread, to potted cheese (Stilton, port and cream served on hot toast) and Waldorf salad. Main courses see a choice of six fish dishes with, perhaps, grilled trout wrapped in bacon, or scampi poached in a white wine and cream sauce with brown rice and salad. There is also a vegetarian dish of the day and other enticements such as beef casseroled in ale, chicken in oatmeal with a mild, creamy mustard sauce and spicy lamb chop. Real ales are on tap in the bar, where tea, coffee and snacks are also served. Home-made pies, nine sorts of ploughman's lunches, daily specials and filled rolls, such as red salmon and cucumber, all feature.

The Robin Hood

Tel: 01-363-3781

The Ridgeway, Botany Bay, Enfield. Situated on the A1005 between Potters Bar & Enfield

Hertfordshire

THE GEORGE AND DRAGON

High Street, Watton-at-Stone.
Tel: (0920) 830285

Hours: Open for lunch and dinner (last orders 9.30pm). Closed Sat lunch/Sun evening/Mon. Bar meals.
Average Prices: A la Carte £18; Sun lunch £12.50; snacks from £1.
Wines: House wine £4 per bottle.

The George and Dragon was first licensed in 1603 and became, in turn, a butcher's shop and coal merchant's yard. For the last 16 years it has been run by Kevin and Christine Dinnin and today its popularity stems from its wide and imaginative menu which changes regularly. The inn itself has a very homely feel with its bay windows, warm carpeting and large inglenook fireplace. The daily newspapers are there for the browsing. In the bar, real ales accompany salads, sandwiches, the celebrated George and Dragon smokey (flakey smoked haddock topped with a tomato concasse, gratinated and finished under the grill) and a range of other hot and cold dishes, such as sweet and sour pork on savoury rice, seafood thermidor and paupiettes of smoked salmon, filled with a mix of avocado and cream cheese. Fresh fish is always readily available and features on the restaurant menu, too, where dishes are generally English – for example breast of duck in a rich red wine sauce and rack of English lamb with rosemary. Home-made puddings conclude.

THE GEORGE
& DRAGON
WATTON-AT-STONE

Ware (0920)
830285

Hertfordshire

THE CASANOVA RESTAURANT

1 Bircherley Green, Hertford. Tel: (0992) 550519/550632

Hours: Open for dinner (last orders 11.30pm). Closed Sun evening.

Average Prices: A la Carte £20-£25; Sun lunch £12.50.

Wines: House wine £6.50 per bottle.

The Casanova Restaurant aims to seduce its customers with a romantic riverside setting and lavish décor. The 42-seater restaurant combines basket-work chairs, fresh flowers, marquee-style drapes and contrasting tones of pink and grey. It is run by partners Pasquale Azzato and Gianni Boscaro who provide a predominantly Italian menu with French touches. Begin, perhaps, with sfogliata di salmone e asparagi (puff pastry with salmon and asparagus in a hollandaise sauce), or avocado mousse with crab and prawns. The main course sees a varied array of fish dishes with, for example, salmone al vermouth (fresh salmon poached in dry vermouth and glazed with cream and tarragon) and gamberoni del Pacifico Casanova (Pacific prawns Casanova-style). There are also meat dishes such as piccata di vitello boschetto (veal escalope sautéed with butter and three different kinds of mushrooms). The wine list incorporates popular European labels, some vintage ports and cocktails. To conclude there is also traditional Italian coffee. Parties and functions for up to 100 guests are catered for upstairs. Major credit cards welcome.

Hertfordshire

THE OLD BARGE

2 The Folly, Hertford. Tel: (0992) 581871
Hours: Open for coffee, lunch and dinner (last orders 9pm). Closed Sun evening.
Average Prices: Bar meals £4.50 (lunch), £8 (dinner).

A combination of real ales and traditional home-cooking makes The Old Barge a popular riverside pub. At lunch and dinner time there is a daily specials board to complement the main menu which sees steak, poultry, fish and vegetarian dishes served, along with a selection of burgers and cold platters. Choose perhaps a Big Tel (burger with bacon, melted cheese, lettuce, onion, cucumber and tomato) or a swordfish steak.

Public House & Restaurant

THE OLD BARGE

ON THE RIVER LEE AT HERTFORD

Traditional ales, wines and spirits
Meals served six days a week, lunchtime and evenings, Mon-Sat

2 The Folly, Hertford. Tel: (0992) 581871

LE GARDE MANGER

8 Arena Parade, Letchworth. Tel: (0462) 682127
Hours: Open for lunch and dinner (last orders 10.30pm).
Average Prices: A la Carte £22; Sun lunch £5.95.

Fresh fish is delivered daily to this provincially French restaurant and reflected in dishes such as smoked mackerel Raifort (with a hollandaise sauce) for a starter and tagliatelle Ambassador (with smoked salmon, cream and mushrooms) for the main course. Alternatively try tournedos Rossini, followed by apple snow (apple puree with cream and port for dessert). John and Yvonne McDonald are the hosts.

Le Garde Manger
RESTAURANT FRANÇAIS

8 Arena Parade
Letchworth. Tel: (0462) 682127

Hertfordshire

THE OLD BULL INN

High Street, Royston. Tel: (0763) 242003
Hours: *Open for coffee, lunch, tea and dinner (last orders 9.30pm). Closed Sun evening. Bar meals.*
Average Prices: *A la Carte £14; Sun lunch £7.50; snacks from £3.95.*
Wines: *House wine £5.25 per bottle.*

The Old Bull Inn first served as a coaching inn during the 17th century and has recently been refitted by well-known local brewers Charles Wells to update it to the needs of the 1990's. There is now, for example, an oak room and ballroom purposefully designed for conferences, functions and banquets. The restaurant menu is traditionally French, starting with champignon ciboulette (button mushrooms served with a chive and cream sauce), melon gondola (melon wedge on orange sorbet) and chicken and spinach pancakes, covered in a light cheese sauce. For the main course there are fish dishes, such as salmon dieppoise (salmon steak poached in white wine and bay leaves, with a prawn and tomato sauce); poultry dishes, such as chicken Josephine (sauce of white wine, diced peppers, mushrooms, herbs and cream), or steaks, au poivre, for example, with garlic bread. Vegetarian diners might try a nut crumble or vegetarian lasagne. These may be followed by a selection of hot or cold sweets, with coffee and mints or tea to finish. Real ales are available from the bar and there is accommodation in 11 rooms.

High Street
Royston
Tel: (0763) 242003

25

Hertfordshire

REDCOATS FARMHOUSE HOTEL

Redcoats Green, near Hitchin. Tel: (0438) 729500
Hours: Open for lunch and dinner (last orders 9pm).
Bar meals lunchtime, except Sat/Sun.
Average Prices: A la Carte 20; snacks from £3.
Wines: House wine £6.50 per bottle.

Visitors wishing to explore rural Hertfordshire could not find a more appropriate place to stay than at Redcoats. This 15th century farmhouse, with some Victorian additions, is surrounded by four acres of grounds which include kitchen gardens where the hotel grows its own vegetables. The pleasantly comfortable air of the countryside permeates the hotel and there are three dining rooms which cater for a variety of occasions, from evening meals to private parties. Indeed, celebrations are a speciality of the chef, who enjoys crafting new dishes and planning the menus. Typical examples of his style are hot crab ramekins (hot pots of crab topped with Parmesan) and galia melon with fresh mint sorbet, for starters. Main courses include duck breast with a fresh mango purée, roast rack of lamb with Louisette sauce (ham, cucumber, mint and cream) and fresh sea bass stuffed with fennel and lemon. Desserts range from spotted dick and butterscotch pancakes to lemon cream crunch, and there is a wine list of 188 labels. Weekend breaks, taking in Friday dinner and Sunday breakfast, have been proving very popular.

REDCOATS GREEN, NR. HITCHIN, HERTS. TEL: (0438) 729500

Hertfordshire

THE BELL INN AND MOTEL

High Street, Codicote, Hitchin. Tel: (0438) 820278
Hours: Open for coffee, lunch, tea and dinner (last orders 10.15pm). Bar meals.
Average Prices: A la Carte £12.50; Sun lunch £6.95; snacks from £1.20.
Wines: House wine £6.95 per bottle.

The Bell, standing on the B625 Welwyn-Hitchin road, makes a welcoming sight, with its splashes of red on whitewashed walls. The inn has been totally refurbished and also has attached motel accommodation. Dining is traditionally à la carte, with a particularly spectacular finish provided by the desserts. Start with orange California (shell of orange filled with chicken, pineapple and celery, on a bed of fresh orange slices), prawn and crab stick cocktail, served with a wedge of lemon and brown bread, or chef's home-made soup of the day. For the main course there is veal cutlet in a light sauce with rosemary, St Clement's chicken (roasted with an orange and lemon sauce and a hint of brandy) and grilled fresh salmon steak with parsley butter and lemon wedges. Desserts are something of a speciality and along with the gâteaux and cheesecakes is an ice cream cocktail menu presenting an inventive assortment of unusual flavours. From the bar are hot and cold snacks, basket meals and open sandwiches. Real ales too.

THE BELL INN & MOTEL High Street, Codicote. Tel: (0438) 820278

Hertfordshire

CLARIDGES

49 High Street, Bovingdon. Tel: (0442) 833243
Hours: Open for dinner. Lunches Wed-Fri bookings only.
Average Prices: A la Carte £13; house wine £6.25 per bottle.

Claridges serves a varied and interesting menu of regularly changed Continental dishes with, for example as starters, a Prawn Shipwreck or brandied stuffed mushrooms with a cream and cognac sauce. Fish is a popular main course dish, with fresh salmon on a bed of spinach in a lobster and brandy sauce as one possible choice. There is a vegetarian menu with, for example, puff pastry filled with broccoli, walnuts and Gruyère cheese with a herb and tomato coulis. Live jazz featured every Sunday evening.

Claridges RESTAURANT

49 High Street, Bovingdon, Herts.
Telephone: Hemel Hempstead
(0442) 833243

GUSTY'S CARVERY AT THE KING'S ARMS

147 High Street, Berkhamsted. Tel: (0442) 866595
Hours: Open for Sun lunch and dinner. Bar lunches Mon-Sat.
Average Prices: Carvery £8.50; bar meals £2.25.

King Louis XVIII of France once frequented this 18th century inn, leading to much local speculation about the virtue of the innkeeper's daughter. The latter replied that the only king's arms she knew was the inn owned by her father. Today, snacks and real ales are served from the bar, and there is a popular carvery upstairs. Here there is a choice between three roasts, the chef's steak and kidney pie and a vegetarian dish. 25 hors d'oeuvre and a sweet trolley.

GUSTY'S CARVERY
AT THE
KING'S ARMS
147 HIGH STREET
BERKHAMSTED
HERTS
Telephone: (0442) 866595

Hertfordshire

THE GALLERIA BAR BRASSERIE

145 High Street, Berkhamsted.
Tel: (0442) 873424

Hours: *Open for coffee, lunch and dinner (last orders 10.30pm, 10pm Sun).*

Average Prices: *A la Carte £5-£10.*

Wines: *House wine £5.25 per bottle.*

Berkhamsted grew up along the old coaching route from London to Birmingham, now the A41, which forms its broad High Street. The Galleria has been open since September 1988 in a building dating back to the 17th century (the former Allcock and Brown public house). The £330,000 refurbishment has resulted in two dining floors which are linked by a mezzanine level (a projecting balcony over the main floor), and the whole establishment has a lively, contemporary atmosphere. Its fun menu is large and flexible with a choice between snacks and full meals. Pasta, stir-fry, vegetarian and traditional pies and casseroles all feature. For starters try peel'n'eat prawns, smoked salmon, baked Camembert on a fruit platter, deep-fried stuffed mushrooms or a selection of loaded potato skins. For the main course there is chicken and asparagus pie, shark steak with a spicy avocado sauce, or stir-fry pork and mange-tout. The menu is accompanied by an equally extensive wine and cocktail list. The dining area seats 44 and all leading credit cards are accepted.

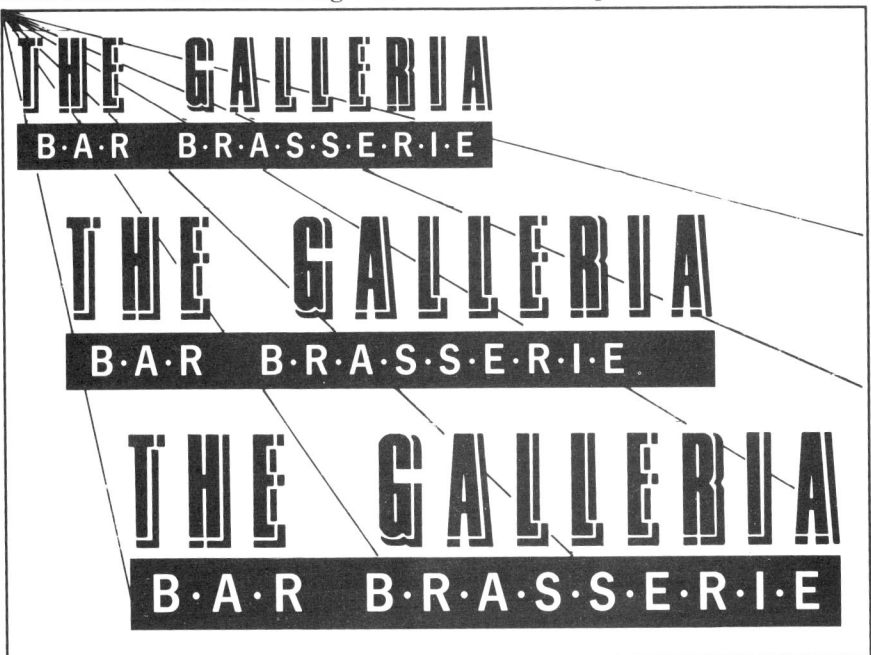

Hertfordshire

THE PENNY FARTHING RESTAURANT

296-298 High Street, Berkhamsted. Tel: (0442) 872828
Hours: *Open for coffee, lunch, tea and dinner.*
Average Prices: *A la Carte £16; light lunches £7; Sun lunch £11.75.*
Wines: *House wine £6.25 per bottle.*

The Penny Farthing Restaurant is run by David Barnett and Austin Smith who have built up its popularity by their attention to detail. Customers are always treated, free of charge at the beginning of a meal, to hot crusty loaf with crispy crudités and an avocado dip. The main menu is extensive, covering fish, grills, vegetarian dishes and specialities. Starters include deep-fried Camembert with a gooseberry sauce and Penny Farthing prawnbreaker (half pint mug of shell-on prawns served with three dips and a lemon wedge). For a main course dish there is Scotch salmon (poached in a fish stock and served with lime and chive butter), veal escalope (with a blended peach and Drambuie sauce), rack of lamb (with a special sauce made from sour cream blended with mint and redcurrant) and, for the very hungry, the 'Dallas Dinner' (two pound rump steak topped with two fried eggs and served with pots of mustard, pepper and a barbecue sauce). The sweet menu is appetising for both chocaholics and the health conscious. Try Hollywood Bowl (a concoction of pistachio, mocha chocolate and strawberry ice cream with fruit salad, marshmallow and meringue, topped with whipped cream and a chocolate sauce).

THE RESTAURANT WITH ROOMS

Hertfordshire

CALENDARS CAFE BAR AND RESTAURANT
657 St Albans Road, Garston, Watford.
Tel: (0923) 672310
Hours: Open 12 noon-11.30pm every day.
Average Prices: A la Carte £14; Sun lunch £5.50; snacks from £1.45.
Wines: House wine £5.75 per bottle.

Calendars is a cosmopolitan and upbeat restaurant, both in its décor and cooking. It has an open plan design and is set out on four levels with a cocktail bar on the third. The menu itself makes interesting reading, not only for its range of dishes, but also for its captions and photographs. The various sections cover pasta, Cajun, fajita, snacks and salad dishes. There is also a section for breakfasts, where it is possible to start the day American-style with waffles and maple syrup or Mexican-style with a scrambled egg tortilla. A full lunch or evening meals begin with appetisers like Pick'n'Mix (for two), crispy loaded potato skins, Calendars' mushrooms, Louisiana chicken wings and bar-b-q spare ribs. Moving on to the main course, there are enchiladas, burgers, Cajun chicken grills and dishes such as London Broil (rump steak marinated in Worcester sauce, char-grilled and served with a herb and mushroom sauce) and Chicken and Friends (marinated in a light teriyaki sauce of lemon and pineapple, char-grilled and covered with sliced ham, melted cheese and a pineapple ring). For dessert, try the Extravaganza (fresh fruit, ice cream, marshmallow, cherry topping, nuts and coconut).

657 St. Albans Road
Garston, Watford
Tel: (0923) 672310

31

Hertfordshire/Buckinghamshire

DEAN PARK HOTEL

30-40 St Albans Road, Watford. Tel: (0923) 229212
Hours: Open for lunch and dinner. Closed Sat lunchtime.
Average Prices: A la Carte £20; Table d'Hôte £13; Sun lunch £9.75.

Dean Park Hotel is situated in the town centre, near the station. Its restaurant can be found on the first floor in a spacious room, decorated in light grey with pink linen. Dishes are French and feature fish, with Dover sole Colbert; flambés, with entrecôte Diane, and meat, with duck in a green peppercorn sauce and chateaubriand (for two). There's a special vintage selection on the wine list.

DEAN PARK HOTEL

- LUXURY ROOMS
ALL WITH PRIVATE FACILITIES
- SUPERB RESTAURANT ● TWO BARS
- EASY PARKING
- MINUTES AWAY FROM M1 and M25

FOR DETAILS AND COLOUR BROCHURE

TEL· WATFORD (0923)229212

30/40 St. Albans Road, Watford, Herts WD1 1RN

THE ARISTOCRAT

1-3 Wendover Road. Aylesbury. Tel: (0296) 434706
Hours: Open for lunch and dinner (last orders 10pm). Closed Sun evening.
Average Prices: Bar snacks £1-£3.50; wine £4.80 per bottle.

The recently refurbished Aristocrat is a traditional pub serving real ales and with a pleasant garden to the rear. Where the cooking is concerned, Teresa Smith provides a varied menu that changes daily and includes pub favourites such as steak and kidney pie, chilli con carne, lasagne, spaghetti and chicken oriental. There are also barbecues during the summer months.

The Aristocrat

Open 11am-11pm
Tuesday-Saturday
Sunday Normal Hours
Monday 11-2.30 5.30-11pm

Wendover Road, Aylesbury Tel: (0296) 434706

32

Buckinghamshire

HARTWELL HOUSE

                        Hartwell, Aylesbury.
                        Tel: (0296) 747444
Hours: *Open for coffee, lunch, tea and dinner (last orders 9.45pm).*
Average Prices: *A la Carte £30; Table d'Hôte £25; Sun lunch £18.*
Wines: *House wine £9.50 per bottle.*

Hartwell House is the latest acquisition by The Historic House Hotels group and is distinguished by the fact that, during the early 19th century, it held court to the exiled King Louis XVIII of France. He made a strong impression on the local community and his wife left her mark, too, taking pleasure in knocking the heads off figurines adorning the staircase. A 20th century restorer replaced them with the heads of recent notables like Winston Churchill. The hotel has all the grandeur and style expected of the company and has also acquired the talents of chef Aidan McCormack, who won wide acclaim at sister establishment Middlethorpe Hall in York. His style is modern and dishes are imaginatively conceived and attractively presented. Specialities include a hot shellfish sausage with broad beans in a butter sauce, followed by breast of duck roasted with turnips in a white wine and caramel sauce and concluded with desserts such as assorted red berries in vanilla ice cream with a kirsch sabayon and the traditionally-English treacle tart. All major credit cards accepted.

Buckinghamshire

PADRINI

17-19 Walton Road, Aylesbury. Tel: (0296) 23486
Hours: Open for lunch and dinner (last orders 9.45pm).
Closed Sun/Mon lunch.
Average Prices: A la Carte £16; house wine £6.25 per bottle.

Standing opposite Walton Pond, Padrini is a welcoming Italian restaurant offering traditional home-cooking from its Italian-born owners. Popular dishes include smoked salmon lasagne, duck with amaretto liqueur and toasted almonds, and veal Fantasia (escalope with fresh asparagus topped with Bel Paese cheese). For a dessert try bavarese de chocolate.

B'S RESTAURANT

Risborough Road, Stoke Mandeville. Tel: (029 661) 3637.
Hours: Open for lunch and dinner (last orders 8.30pm Mon, 9.30pm Tues-Sat). Closed Sun evening/Mon lunch.
Average Prices: A la Carte £11.95; Sun lunch £8.50.

B's, a barn-style restaurant, is situated on the A4010 Stoke Mandeville-Princes Risborough road, behind Belmore Hotel. The menu changes weekly, offering interesting cuisine, from succulent steaks to the 'Chef's Special'. Vegetarians thoughtfully catered for. Husband and wife, Ken and Lu, have worked hard at creating a friendly and informal atmosphere in a beautiful Chiltern setting. Credit cards accepted.

B's Restaurant
Risborough Road
Stoke Mandeville
Aylesbury, Bucks
Restaurant: Stoke Mandeville (029 661) 3637

Buckinghamshire

THE OLD SWAN

High Street, Cheddington. Tel: (0296) 668226
Hours: Open for coffee, lunch and dinner (last orders 10pm). Closed Sun/Mon evening.
Average Prices: A la Carte £10; Sun lunch £7.50; snacks from £1.20.

The Old Swan is a 17th century, thatched, country village family pub with a large locals' bar and a separate dining room serving a selection of traditional home-cooked dishes. Fish is a menu speciality with, for example, grilled rainbow trout and Dover sole with a tartare sauce. There are also open sandwiches, ploughman's, jacket potatoes and vegetarian dishes. Attractive garden and children's play area.

The Old Swan
High Street
Cheddington
Nr. Leighton Buzzard
Bedfordshire
Tel: (0296) 668226

THE BOOT

Soulbury, near Leighton Buzzard. Tel: (052 527) 433
Hours: Open for coffee, lunch and dinner.
Average Prices: A la Carte £8.50; Sun lunch £7.75; snacks from £1.50.

The Boot is a trim Georgian inn with an abundance of character from its inglenook fireplace, antique pictures and stone floors. Real ales accompany a traditional value for money menu which offers home-made pies and puddings, and dishes such as local duck in an orange sauce and curried prawns with poppadoms. There's also a family room and an attractive Tudor cottage to the rear.

The Boot
51 HIGH ROAD,
SOULBURY,
LEIGHTON BUZZARD,
BEDFORDSHIRE.
TEL: (052 527) 433

Buckinghamshire

THE HALFWAY HOUSE

London Road, Wendover Dene.
Tel: (0296) 624878
Hours: Open for lunch and dinner (last orders 9.30pm).
Closed Mon. Bar meals.
Average Prices: A la Carte £10; Sun lunch £4.95; snacks from £2.95.
Wines: House wine £6.75 per bottle.

The Halfway House is situated along the A413, halfway between Amersham and Aylesbury. It is a convenient stopping off point for both passing businessmen and walkers using the nearby Ridgeway path that wends its way through the Chiltern Hills. The inn dates from the 18th century and is composed of a series of converted cottages, with a large garden to the rear that has children's amusements. The inn also has a well-established reputation for its traditional, home-cooked food. Starters begin with garlic mushrooms and Portuguese sardines, followed by steak and kidney pudding, beef bourguignon and veal. To finish, try some of the popular chocolate and brandy pudding. Vegetarian dishes too. Sunday lunch is particularly popular. From the bar there are real ales which include Charles Wells' Eagle and Bombardier and bar snacks such as lasagne, cottage pie, chicken curry, moussaka and steak baps. Accommodation is catered for in five rooms, both Visa and Access cards are accepted and there is ample parking.

THE HALFWAY HOUSE
**WENDOVER DENE
BUCKINGHAMSHIRE
TELEPHONE 0296 624878**

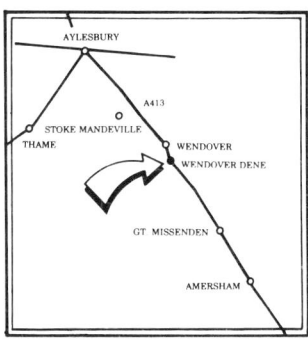

Buckinghamshire

THE PHEASANT INN
Ballinger Common, near Great Missenden.
Tel: (024 020) 236
Hours: Open for lunch and dinner. Closed Sun evening.
Average Prices: A la Carte £10-£12; light lunches from £2.50.

Overlooking the village common and cricket pitch, The Pheasant is a traditional inn with a beamed bar and the added attractions of a conservatory and sunny patio. Its appetising and realistically-priced menu has 'Beginnings' such as avocado and crab Mornay, 'Middles' such as chicken almondine and summer pudding for 'Ends'. Fine wines and real ales. Set at the heart of the Chilterns.

PHEASANT INN

BALLINGER COMMON,
GREAT MISSENDEN, BUCKS.   TEL: (024020) 236

KING WILLIAM IV
Speen, near Aylesbury. Tel: (024 028) 329
Hours: Open for lunch and dinner. Closed Sun evening.
Average Prices: A la Carte £15-£20.

A farmhouse, during the 17th century, and now an inn standing by the village green, King William IV has two attractively decorated restaurants, one non-smoking. The food is exquisitely prepared by three chefs and includes dishes such as fresh salmon with prawns and asparagus and chicken with wild mushrooms and a Chablis sauce. The wine list covers over 30 labels; real ales from the bar too. Terrace for summer drinking.

King William IV

Hampden Road,
Speen, Bucks.

Tel: 024 028 329

Buckinghamshire

THE OLD PLOW INN AND RESTAURANT
Flowers Bottom, Speen, near High Wycombe.
Tel: (024 028) 300
Hours: Open for lunch and dinner (last orders 9.30pm).
Closed Sat lunch/Sun evening/Mon. Bar meals lunchtime only.
Average Prices: A la Carte £25; Table d'Hôte lunch £13.95; Sun Lunch £17.50. House wines £8.95 per bottle.

The arrival of Malcolm Cowan and his wife, Olivia, brings new life to this popular inn. Malcolm worked on the Queen Elizabeth, at the Ritz and finally as head chef at Maxim's de Paris in London before deciding to branch out on his own. His style of cooking is modern Anglo-French and evidenced in starters such as warm scallop and mussel salad with grapefruit and smoked bacon, and main courses which include roasted duck breast with honey, sage, chestnuts and red cabbage, and medallions of venison with roasted baby onions, chestnuts and bacon. For a dessert try the old-fashioned lemon tart with two sauces, or honey and ginger ice cream in a brandy snap tulip with mango and peach coulis. Particular care and thought is invested in the wine list which also features 10 and 20 year-old bas armagnacs and Pinot des Charantes dessert wines. Lunches are available in the 16th century oak-beamed bar and include Scotch beef steak and Guinness pie, crispy duck legs with a ginger and plum sauce, and home-made white chocolate ice cream for dessert. Real ales too.

The Old Plow Inn and Restaurant

Flowers Bottom, Speen,
Telephone: (024 028) 300

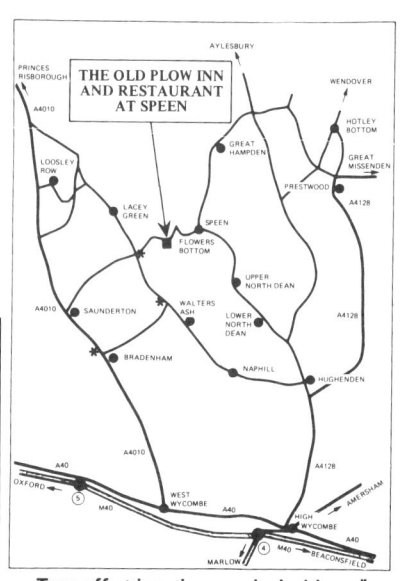

Turn off at junctions marked with an *

Buckinghamshire

SIMPSONS BRASSERIE
Market Square, Princes Risborough. Tel: (084 44) 2690
Hours: Open 10am for coffee, lunch and dinner (last orders 9.30pm). Closed all day Mon, and Sun and Tues evenings.
Average Prices: A la Carte £14-£16; Sun lunch £7.50.

Hundreds of wine bottles and mirrors of all shapes and sizes cover the walls and complement the restful, candlelit, atmosphere of Simpson's, where the seasonally-based menu is Continentally eclectic. Seafood en brochette, poussin Elizabethan and pheasant and beef kebabs are accompanied by crispy vegetables in the French style. Always an informal affair, Sunday lunch, with a table d'hote and children's Menu, is a wonderfully relaxing interlude.

SIMPSON'S
Brasserie

The restaurant that takes a slightly different view of life

2a Duke Street, Princes Risborough. Tel: (084 44) 2690

THE BERNARD ARMS HOTEL
Great Kimble, near Aylesbury. Tel: (084 44) 6173
Hours: Open for coffee, lunch and dinner. Closed Sun eve.
Average Prices: A la Carte £8.50; Sun lunch £7.75; snacks from £1.50.

The Bernard Arms is a small family-run hotel set amid the beechwood hills of the Chilterns. Home-made and traditional dishes partner the country setting. Choose between roast duckling in an orange sauce, chicken in a red wine sauce with mushrooms, lasagne and Dover sole. Snacks include open sandwiches, ploughman's lunches and jacket potatoes. Real ales in the bar and accommodation in seven rooms, each with private shower.

The Bernard Arms Hotel
Great Kimble, Nr. Aylesbury
Tel: (084 44) 6173

Buckinghamshire

THE ROSE AND CROWN INN AND RESTAURANT

Wycombe Road, Saunderton, near Princes Risborough.
Tel: (084 44) 5299/3660

Hours: Open for coffee, lunch and dinner (last orders 9.30pm, 10pm Fri/Sat). Closed Sat/Mon lunch and Sun evening.
Average Prices: A la Carte £19; Sun lunch £9.75; snacks 85p.
Wines: House wine £6.25 per bottle.

Saunderton lies to the side of the A4010, running from Aylesbury to High Wycombe, and has hung onto its traditional Chiltern character. There are many popular strolls through the beechwoods of the area and it is also pleasant to sit in the landscaped gardens of The Rose and Crown which has a patio for summer drinking. Inside, the Beechwood Restaurant has the airy and sunny appeal of a conservatory. The menu is traditional with a leaning towards seafood, a salad of crustacea, set on an edible seaweed, to start, for example. Alternatively, begin with crown of seasonal melon, filled with mango and Grand Marnier sorbet and finished with champagne. The menu is seasonally based and on the main course there may be dishes such as boned, stuffed quail, served with an apple and cider sauce and garnished with caramelised apples, or supreme of Gressingham duck, set on blackcurrant and cassis. Sweets from the trolley, a selection of English and French farmhouse cheeses and coffee and petits fours conclude.

ROSE AND CROWN INN

HOTEL AND
RESTAURANT

Wycombe Road
Saunderton
(Nr. Princes Risborough)
Tel: 084 44 5299/3660

THE BLUE FLAG

Cadmore End, High Wycombe.
Tel: (0494) 881183
Hours: Open for lunch and dinner (last orders 9.45pm).
Average Prices: A la Carte £14; Sun lunch £8.50; snacks from £1.
Wines: House wine £6.50 per bottle.

The Hambledown Valley is dotted with villages whose names incorporate the word 'end', a reference to the many lanes which seem to lead nowhere. The Blue Flag is one of its traditional country inns revelling in oak beaming and old inglenook fireplaces, and with brass ornaments along the walls. There are real ales from the bar including Webster's Yorkshire Bitter, Boddingtons from Manchester and Ruddles from Leicestershire, in addition to a wide selection of popular bar meals. The list of over 20 dishes has home-made steak and kidney pie, chilli con carne, fresh haddock, half duck, cold lobster and lasagne verdi with garlic bread. The inn has its own smokerie and fresh fish features prominently on the menu with, for example, haddock, lobster, scallops, shrimps and salmon. The accompanying wine list features the most popular European labels. Accommodation is also provided, in 16 bedrooms with a special ground floor suite for disabled visitors. Access, Visa, Amex and Diner's Club cards are all taken.

The Blue Flag

Cadmore End, High Wycombe. Tel: 0494 881183

Buckinghamshire

THE COMPLEAT ANGLER
Marlow Bridge, Bisham Road, Marlow.
Tel: (062 84) 4444
Hours: Open for lunch and dinner (last orders 10pm, 10.30pm Sat). Bar meals lunchtime.
Average Prices: A la Carte £30; Sun lunch £24.50; snacks from £7.50.
Wines: House wine £12.50 per bottle.

The Compleat Angler can lay claim to many things. It has a literary heritage, with Izaak Walton having written his famous treatise on fishing here during the early 17th century, and also enjoys one of the best possible settings on the Thames, overlooking Marlow weir and the famous suspension bridge. The Valaisan Restaurant is furnished with a sophisticated country elegance, intermingling oak beaming and tie-back curtains. Christian Chaumette is the chef in charge of the largely French menu which begins with terrine de sanglier, sauce Oxford (a wild boar terrine with an orange and port sauce), or saumon fumé d'Ecosse (Scottish smoked salmon with capers and onions). The main course sees a choice between poissons and entrées. The selection here includes darne de turbot poché au beurre blanc (darne of turbot poached and served with beurre blanc) and medaillons de chevreuil aux poires (medallions of venison accompanied by poached pears). During the summer months there are few things more pleasant than relaxing out on the long river terrace, watching the sun go down over the water.

The Compleat Angler Hotel

Marlow Bridge, Marlow, Buckinghamshire. Telephone: Marlow (06-284) 4444

Buckinghamshire

CHEQUERS INN, HOTEL AND RESTAURANT

                        Kiln Lane, Wooburn Common. Tel: (062 85) 29575
Hours: Open for coffee, lunch, tea and dinner.
Average Prices: A la Carte £15; Sun lunch £13.95; snacks from £2.
Wines: House wine £4.95 per bottle.

In 1975, Peter and John Roehrig took over the shell of what had been a 17th century inn and have since transformed it into a relaxing, small country hotel. The bar mixes old beaming and brick, taken from a local kiln, with various bric-a-brac including a display of old pewter mugs and an open log fire. The restaurant serves both classical and French cuisine and fresh local ingredients are always used. The menus, both à la carte and table d'hôte, change frequently and may include starters such as oak-smoked salmon with granary bread or chicken livers and water chestnuts wrapped in bacon with a mustard and raspberry dressing. For the main course there is a choice between scampi coated with paprika and mushrooms served with pilau rice, prime Scotch sirloin steak with a Meaux mustard and red wine sauce, or, for vegetarians, red kidney beans in a tandoori sauce with wild rice. For private dining there is an adjacent room, seating 50 guests, that is decorated to resemble a Victorian parlour.

THE HIT OR MISS INN

                        Penn Street Village, near Amersham. Tel: (0494) 713109
Hours: Open for lunch and dinner (last orders 9.30pm).
                        Closed Sun evening/Mon. Bar meals.
Average Prices: A la Carte £18; Sun lunch £14.95; snacks from £1.80.

The Hit or Miss cricket team play on the village green opposite this wisteria-clad 16th century inn. The village and inn are both rich in the atmosphere of times past, whilst cooking is seasonal and to order. Start with grilled fresh sardines, followed by côte de boeuf or butter-filled leg of lamb from the grill. The wine list covers 42 labels and there are real ales from the bar. Specials too and snacks such as stuffed mushrooms.

The Hit or Miss Inn

(FREE HOUSE)

Penn Street Village Nr Amersham

Tel: High Wycombe (0494) 713109

Buckinghamshire

The Bull Hotel

The Bull Hotel, Oxford Road, Gerrards Cross, Bucks.

TEL 0753 885995 TELEX 847747 FAX 0753 885504

DE VERE HOTELS

THE BULL HOTEL
Oxford Road, Gerrards Cross.
Tel: (0753) 885995
Hours: Open for coffee, lunch, tea and dinner (last orders 9.30pm).
Bar meals lunchtime, except Saturday and Sunday.
Average Prices: A la Carte £19.50; Table d'Hôte £16.50;
Sunday lunch £15.75; snacks from £2.50.
Wines: House wine £7.95 per bottle.

The Bull Hotel is situated in the charming location of Gerrards Cross. Built as a coaching inn in the 17th century, it has retained its 'olde worlde' atmosphere. Steeped in history, one of the hotel's two bars is named after the most notorious highwayman of the time, Jack Shrimpton.

The hotel takes its name from the times when a Saxon lord by the name of Shobbington successfully defeated a 1000-strong Norman army by charging them with herds of bulls. In more peaceful times The Bull is now a 96 luxury-bedroomed establishment with conference and banqueting facilities and a restaurant tastefully decorated in pinks, blues and green.

The hotel offers traditional fayre at lunchtimes, such as steak, kidney and mushroom pudding or perhaps roast beef and Yorkshire pudding that is carved at the table. Before going into dinner, guests can take a drink in the Cocktail Bar or relax on the patio overlooking the beautiful gardens and ornamental pond, complete with fish and a fountain. The French à la carte selection features appetizers such as a pastry case filled with mixed peppers and a chicken mousseline, served with tomato and asparagus, and finishes with strawberry biscuit stacked in three layers, filled with strawberries and double cream, for dessert. In between there are many main course temptations: fillets of trout poached in a red wine sauce, garnished with button onions and mushrooms, are one possibility, or try veal chop, charcoal-grilled and garnished with parsley butter and lemon. Alternatively, there is breast of chicken filled with fresh mango in breadcrumbs and coconut, or sautéed strips of calves' liver, flamed in sherry and covered in a rich meat sauce. Vegetarians are also well looked-after.

For lighter snacks the Jack Shrimpton Bar, complete with oak beams and a log fire, is an ideal setting for lunch, with a cold buffet selection or hot dishes such as apple and cider hotpot and Cumberland sausage with onion sauce and new potatoes.

Kingsclere Publications produces a varied list of publications in the **Where to Eat** *series which cover areas as far apart as Scotland, The Channel Islands and Ireland.*

Buckinghamshire

The Royal Standard of England
Free House

Known The World Over

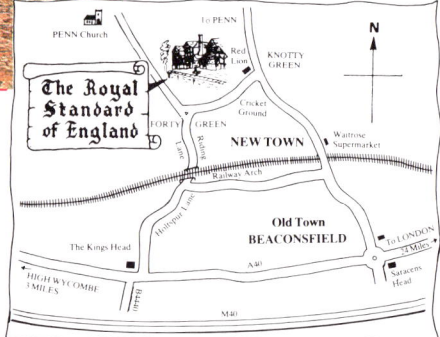

The King Charles Room

Forty Green, Beaconsfield
Telephone: 0494 673382

46

Buckinghamshire

THE ROYAL STANDARD OF ENGLAND

Forty Green, Beaconsfield.
Tel: (0494) 673382
Hours: Open for coffee, lunch and dinner (last orders 10pm).
Bar meals.
Average Prices: A la Carte £8; Sun lunch £8.50; snacks from £1.50.
Wines: House wine £4.50 per bottle.

The Royal Standard of England is a uniquely historic inn which also enjoys one of the most attractive settings in the whole of the Chilterns. Beloved of novelists like G K Chesterton and Enid Blyton, the countryside surrounding Beaconsfield was once thickly wooded and is now dotted with tiny villages.

The inn's title was granted by Charles II in recognition of the refuge it gave him on his flight to France after the battle of Worcester in 1651. It still remains much as he would have seen it. The outside is pleasing through the very irregularity of its architecture: a sloping tiled roof, jumbled brick and stone walls, and bay windows, some of which incorporate stained glass from London churches blitzed during WWII. A low stone wall, running around the front of the inn, shelters a rose garden where chairs are set during the summer months.

The most famous incident in the inn's long history is now commemorated in the King Charles Room which, through painstaking restoration, atmospherically recalls the inn's Medieval origins. The roof is still supported by 11th century rafters and beams run across the room from wall to wall. The walls themselves are plaster and timber, and lined with an assortment of curios to add extra interest. In the lounge bar, for example, sits a large ship's settle that once belonged to the 18th century statesman Edmund Burke.

This living museum forms a pleasantly diverting backdrop to the buffet bar of the King Charles Room. It is renowned for the range of its choice which includes a display of cheeses, home-cooked beef, pork, ham, turkey and chicken, pies, pâtés, quiches and salads. Accompanying these is home-baked bread, and chutney that is made to a 300-year-old house recipe. Summer specialities include Scottish salmon and Cromer crab salad.

Hot meals are also available, with dishes such as traditional beef and oyster pie in Guinness gravy, pork spare ribs in a barbecue sauce, a seafood platter and plaice with prawns in a cheese sauce. A tempting range of desserts concludes, treacle and nut tart and apple pie being two of the options.

Traditional ale has always been a speciality of the inn. The powerful Owd Roger was brewed here by successive landlords for some 400 years and is now prepared for the inn and other outlets by Marston of Burton, who also supply their award-winning Pedigree bitter to The Royal Standard of England.

Buckinghamshire

WHEELERS OF BEACONSFIELD

14 London End, Beaconsfield. Tel: (0494) 677077
Hours: Open for lunch and dinner (last orders 10pm, 10.30pm Fri/Sat). Closed Sun.
Average Prices: A la Carte £19.
Wines: House wine £6.95 per bottle.

The cuisine and atmosphere of Wheelers of St James's in London is complemented by its sister establishment, situated in the old town of Beaconsfield. The bow fronted restaurant is covered with tubs of flowers and is characterized by heavy beaming and an inglenook fireplace within. Fish is the speciality but there is also a children's menu for the under twelves, salads, grills and a vegetarian dish. A good selection is offered such as prawn thermidor, oysters or crab and avocado salad. The main course is wide ranging, with lobster, halibut, plaice, scallops, Scotch salmon, skate, Dover and lemon sole. The choice of sauces is equally extensive to accompany the traditional soles. Scottish salmon is served poached with hollandaise sauce, grilled with béarnaise sauce, or poached with shrimps and asparagus in a white wine sauce. Also on the menu there is a weekly chef's selection which can include such things as a seafood platter, sea bass and monkfish. On Sundays a brunch menu is offered with such specialities as kedgeree and kippers. Desserts feature a Bailey's chocolate cheesecake and locally-made ice creams and sorbets, and the wine list is extensive with an interesting Manager's selection.

Buckinghamshire

THE SHELSWELL INN
Newton Purcell. Tel: (028 04) 401
Hours: Open for coffee, lunch and dinner (last orders 9.30pm). Restaurant closed Sun/Tues evenings. Bar meals.
Average Prices: A la Carte £15; snacks from £1.65.

Originally a coaching inn, The Shelswell Inn has been modernised and refurbished into an attractive inn with a homely garden that includes an adventure playground. Real ales are served from the bar along with hearty bar snacks such as steak and kidney pie, whilst the restaurant offers traditional home-cooking with steaks and roast beef, curries, chilli, stir-fry, etc. Music most Saturday evenings and the first Sunday lunchtime each month.

SHELSWELL INN

Newton Purcell
Tel: 02804 401

Where to Eat FREE !

Here's your chance to help us compile the next edition of WHERE TO EAT for your area – and receive a copy of the guide free of charge!

As knowledgeable diners, you may come across some worthwhile eating places not featured in this edition. We'd like you to tell us about them. In return we will send a copy of the next edition to the first 50 readers who write in with recommendations. Write to:

Where To Eat Free!
Kingsclere Publications Ltd.
Highfield House, 2 Highfield Avenue
Newbury, Berkshire, RG14 5DS

We look forward to hearing from you!

Buckinghamshire

THE BELL INN

Aston Clinton. Tel: (0296) 630252
Hours: Open for lunch, tea and dinner (last orders 9.45pm).
Average Prices: A la Carte £38; Table d'Hôte £16.50; Sun lunch £19.50.
Wines: House wine £6 per bottle.

Originally built to serve as a coaching inn during the 17th century, The Bell today is widely renowned as a high class restaurant with attached accommodation, some of which is situated across the road in the old stables and malthouse block. The rooms look out onto attractive gardens and one room in the main hotel is distinguished by Bavarian hand-painted furniture. The restaurant itself has been highly acclaimed for both its cuisine and setting. Arcadian frescoes give the dining room a refined air which complements the culinary skills of chef Kevin Cape. Classical French methods shine through dishes which begin with salade aphrodite sur son ocean de perles noires à la ville de Reims (a salad of aphrodisiacs served on a bed of caviar and accompanied by champagne). Caviar also features on the main course with dishes such as chou vert de saumon et ses blinis de pomme de terre au caviar (layers of salmon interwoven with cabbage, served with a potato pancake and caviar) and rable de lièvre aux deux sauces (lightly cooked roast fillet of hare, served with a poached pear and a duet of game sauces). The extensive wine list covers over 500 bottles.

THE BELL INN

The Perfect place for . . .

Lunch
Dinner
Luxurious
Accommodation

ASTON CLINTON
TEL: (0296) 630252

THE OLD THATCHED INN AND RESTAURANT

Main Street, Adstock.
Tel: (029 671) 2584

Hours: Open for lunch and dinner (last orders 10pm). Closed Sun evening. Bar meals, except Sun evening.
Average Prices: A la Carte £16; Sun lunch £9.50; snacks from £4.50.
Wines: House wine £6 per bottle.

Just off the A413, linking Buckingham to Aylesbury, is the small self-contained village of Adstock. Its 17th century inn delights the eye with its thatched roof and whitewashed walls strewn with flowers. Within, the atmosphere is homely with the original flagstone floor, numerous horse brasses and a fireplace big enough to stand in. The dining room is furnished with tables of all shapes and its menu changes with the four seasons. Traditional English dishes, with lobster, beef Wellington, Scotch salmon and duckling, regularly feature and vegetarians are also catered for. Bar snacks can be enjoyed and special occasions celebrated in the newly completed conservatory. Dishes here cover seasoned lamb, barbecued pork, chilli con carne and many more. Five real ales are on draught and these include Ruddles County and a guest beer, with mulled wine for the long winter evenings. The inn is also the winner of the Victor Band trophy and holder of 'highly-recommended' certificates four years running for its food and hygiene.

MAIN STREET, ADSTOCK, BUCKS. TEL: (029671) 2584

Buckinghamshire

THE VILLIERS HOTEL
24 Castle Street, Buckingham.
Tel: (0280) 822444/822822
Hours: Open for lunch and dinner (last orders 10.30pm).
Average Prices: A la Carte £12.50 (dinner), £6 (lunch); Sun lunch £5.50.
Wines: House wine £6.50 per bottle.

The Villiers Hotel is a modern new development in Buckingham town centre, but has a traditional approach to comfort. The Cotton Club Restaurant is one of the main highlights and has an interesting twenties art deco design based around the famous Harlem jazz club. The colour scheme is black and white, with odeon chairs, contemporary prints along the walls and jazz music playing quietly in the background. The menu which changes every four months is brasserie-style with, for example, as starters deep-fried Camembert, spare ribs in a spicy barbecue sauce and tagliatelle in a creamy mushroom, fruit and nut sauce. For the main course there is a wide selection of steaks with an accompaniment of sauces and dishes such as wiener schnitzel (veal coated in breadcrumbs and shallow-fried), pork tenderloin (stuffed with seasoned chicken livers and served with a white sauce) and scampi provençale. Dessert features home-made cheesecake and accompanying are a wide range of wines, spirits and soft drinks.

24 Castle Street
Buckingham. Tel: (0280) 822444

DIPALEE TANDOORI

	18 Castle Street, Buckingham.
	Tel: (0280) 813151/813925
Hours:	Open for lunch (last orders 2pm) and dinner (last orders 11.30pm).
Average Prices:	A la Carte £13.50; Table d'Hôte £12.50.
Wines:	House wine £5.10 per bottle.

The Dipalee Tandoori has now been open for eight years and this restaurant has a chain of establishments throughout Buckinghamshire. All are well known for the quality of their dishes and the high standards of service. The Dipalee, for example, won the Victor Band Trophy in 1985, has been a consecutive winner in the Aylesbury Vale District Council's Clean Food Award and is recommended by Les Routiers. Within the restaurant a traditionally exotic Indian décor provides the setting for authentic dishes, skilfully prepared. The main highlight is the house speciality – a khurzi feast for two or four persons. It is a chicken and lamb combination, placed in a creamy spice and yoghurt marinade for at least 24 hours and then roasted for six hours. The long cooking time obviously requires advance notice and 48 hours is preferred. There is also a wide choice of accompanying wines. Major credit cards accepted.

Dipalee Tandoori Restaurant

**18 CASTLE STREET
BUCKINGHAM
Telephone: (0280) 813151/813925**

Buckinghamshire

BARNABY'S CARVERY

The Talbot, London Road, Loughton, Milton Keynes.
Tel: (0908) 666420
Hours: Open for coffee, lunch and dinner. Bar meals.
Average Prices: Carvery £7.95 (2 courses); bar meals from £1.50.
Wines: House wine £5.95 per bottle.

A listed 16th century building, The Talbot stands on the old A5 at Loughton. It has been plushly refurbished to modern expectations and has a popular carvery that aims to provide value for money food and wine. It is decorated in shades of cream and green, which offset the polished chairs and furnishings, and provides three roasts a day that are accompanied by fresh vegetables and potatoes. Preceding the main course is a choice between 16 hot and cold starters and, to finish the meal, there is a range of desserts from £1 more. A reasonably priced selection of wines accompanies. Alternatively, from the bar there are inexpensive snacks and real ales such as Ruddles Best Bitter. Both vegetarians and children are catered for, with the under fives eating free, and during the summer months there are barbecues, too, held in the garden which also has amusements to entertain the kids. Weddings and other functions are professionally catered for and there are occasional speciality evenings, for Mother's Day, Valentine's Day, etc. All major credit cards are accepted.

Barnaby's Carvery

33 London Road, Loughton, Milton Keynes. Tel: (0908) 666420

THE BROUGHTON HOTEL

Broughton Village, Milton Keynes. Tel: (0908) 667726
Hours: *Open for coffee, lunch and dinner (last orders 9.45pm). Closed Sat lunch. Bar meals.*
Average Prices: *A la Carte £20; Table d'Hôte £7; Sun lunch £10; snacks from £1.50.*
Wines: *House wine £5 per bottle.*

The Broughton Hotel is situated on the outskirts of Milton Keynes, two minutes from junction 14 of the M1 and with views out over the rolling Buckinghamshire countryside. The hotel is modern, but its comfort is traditional. In Brooklands Restaurant a rust colour scheme is dominated by a high brick fireplace and selected pictures, all giving a feeling of warmth. The menu itself is French and carefully compiled by Ann and John Barstow. Avocado (half-avocado filled with lobster and topped with a cheese and mustard sauce), or smoked salmon (served the Russian way on hot pancakes with lumpfish roe and sour cream) can be found on the list of starters. Main course dishes include fillet of pink trout (sautéd in butter and served with a cream and chive sauce), breast of duck (sautéd with brandy, sliced and served in a half-baby pineapple that has been poached in white wine) and pheasant (cooked in a wine sauce with port and vegetables). Home-made sweets and speciality coffees conclude. Snacks available in The Kingshead Bar.

Broughton Village, Milton Keynes Tel: (0908) 667726

Buckinghamshire

WOUGHTON HOUSE HOTEL

Woughton-on-the-Green, Milton Keynes.
Tel: (0908) 661919

Hours: Open for coffee, lunch, tea and dinner (last orders 9.45pm, 10.30pm Sat). Bar meals.
Average Prices: Table d'Hôte £13.50/£17.50; Sun lunch £13.50.
Wines: House wine £5.95 per bottle.

Built in the late Victorian era and surrounded by five acres of grounds, Woughton House enjoys a country setting within the city limits of Milton Keynes. The hotel is also only a few minutes away from junction 13 of the M1 and makes a good business venue. There are conference and catering facilities for 120, with a function room and 20 en suite bedrooms. These are accompanied by a restaurant serving a regularly changed Anglo-French menu. Begin with Scotch smoked salmon, or Americaine salade mayonnaise (lettuce, prawns, asparagus and cucumber mayonnaise). Follow on to the main course with a selection between suprême de volaille Maryland (breadcrumbed chicken garnished with bacon, banana, tomato and a sweetcorn fritter), tournedos alsacienne (fillet grilled and served with bacon, sauerkraut and jus-lié) and game casserole (pheasant and venison braised in a rich wine sauce). A separate dessert menu finishes off with freshly made coffee and petits fours. Children are made very welcome and have plenty of garden amusements. Major credit cards accepted.

TEL: (0908) 661919

JAIPUR RESTAURANT

Elder House, 502 Elder Gate, Milton Keynes.
Tel: (0908) 669796/667331
Hours: *Open for lunch and dinner (last orders 10.45pm),*
11pm Fri/Sat).
Average Prices: *A la Carte £12.50; Sunday family buffet lunch £7.95.*
Wines: *House wine £6.95 per bottle.*

The Jaipur, which is situated adjacent to Central Milton Keynes railway station, is an exclusively upmarket Indian Restaurant. It first made its mark when it was opened by an elephant called Maureen, accompanied by television personality Anneka Rice, and has since built up its reputation on a luxurious colonial-style décor and quality cuisine. The cocktail bar and main restaurant are both stylishly decorated in a dusky pink with each table graced by cut glass and real flowers. The menu is wide-ranging with dishes such as lamb pasanda (a dish made from the choicest cuts of lamb which are marinated with fragrant herbs, threaded on skewers and char-grilled) and murgh masala (a Punjabi dish which is made with chicken stewed in a fried onion and tomato gravy, with fresh coriander added just before serving as a contrast). Smart dress is requested in the restaurant – no denims – although take-away meals are also available. All major credit cards are accepted.

Jaipur Restaurant, Station Square, Central Milton Keynes Tel: 0908 669796

Buckinghamshire

HOUSTONS RESTAURANT
The Winter Gardens, 444 Midsummer Boulevard, Milton Keynes. Tel: (0908) 678883
Hours: Open from 11.30am Mon-Sat, 12 noon Sun, for lunch and dinner (last orders 11.30pm, 10.30pm Sun).
Average Prices: A la Carte less than £12; children's menu.
Wines: House wine £7.90 per litre.

The Winter Gardens is one of Milton Keynes' latest and most spectacular developments. A huge canopy of glass covers this leisure complex, overflowing with exotic plants and shrubs. At Houstons it is possible to eat al fresco overlooking the gardens or to experience the taste and atmosphere of Texas within the restaurant itself. Themed around the city of Houston, the space connection is strong and there is the odd petrol pump in attendance too. Appetizers include civichi (marinated scallops and prawns in a lime and Tequila sauce) and buffalo wings (chicken wings in a bar-b-q sauce). Following on from this are dishes such as fajitas (chicken and beef on a bed of grilled onions and peppers, served with guacamole, sour cream, pico de gallo, fresh salsa and warm tortilla flour), barbecue baby back ribs (home-smoked and with a bar-b-q sauce), swordfish steaks, salads and enchiladas. Side dishes include crispy onion rings unusually served as a loaf and for dessert there are home-made cheesecakes, carrot cake, brownies and speciality ice creams. The children's menu has moon burgers, rocket fuel (soft drinks) and ice cream.

444 Midsummer
Boulevard
Central
Milton Keynes
0908 678883

Buckinghamshire

THE POST HOUSE HOTEL
500 Saxon Gate West, Central Milton Keynes.
Tel: (0908) 667722
Hours: Open for coffee, lunch, tea and dinner. Bar meals.
Average Prices: A la Carte £14.50; Sun lunch £7.95; snacks from £2.
Wines: House wine £6.50 per bottle.

Situated in the centre of Milton Keynes, The Post House is characteristic of others in this famous hotel group with its striking modern design and forward looking approach. Accommodation is provided in 163 rooms, all en suite, there are two restaurants and extensive conference facilities. A 'Hungry Bear' menu for children is available from the Atrium Restaurant, which is open all day, whilst the Club House Restaurant specialises in a modern English menu. Dishes are all cooked to order and attractively presented. Starters include three filo baskets with scallops, salmon and lobster in a medley of sauces, a seasonal sorbet, for example rhubarb with a glaze, avocado prawns and bresola (Italian smoked beef). For the main course there is saddle of lamb with a spring onion, tomato and sorrel sauce, ballotine of chicken stuffed with foie gras in a truffle and white wine sauce, and poached or grilled salmon in a watercress sauce. Desserts are from the trolley and include a mix-your-own seasonal fruit salad and Chocolate Indulgence (a rich mousse gâteau). Coffee, snacks and afternoon tea are all served in the lounge.

Post House Hotel

500 Saxon Gate West
Central Milton Keynes
(0908) 667722

Trusthouse
Forte Hotels

Buckinghamshire

TORENZO ITALIAN RESTAURANT AND PIZZERIA
Midsummer Arcade, Milton Keynes. Tel: (0908) 663826
Hours: Open all day, 11.30am-11pm (last orders 9.45pm) Mon-Sat.
Average Prices: A la Carte £8.50 (evening), £7 (lunch).

During the day Torenzo is ideal both for informal business lunches and fast food Italian style. At night the atmosphere subtly changes as the lights are lowered. The menu encompasses home-made pizzas, pasta, speciality dishes and salads. These include scaloppe alla milanese (veal in breadcrumbs), cannelloni, ravioli and tortelloni verdi (spinach pasta stuffed with Ricotta cheese in a cream sauce). Al fresco meals on patio.

Torenzo
ITALIAN RESTAURANT & PIZZERIA
MIDDLETON HALL
158 MIDSUMMER ARCADE
MILTON KEYNES SHOPPING CENTRE
RESERVATIONS
0908 663826

THE BELL AND BEAR
Emberton, near Olney. Tel: (0234) 711565
Hours: Open for coffee, lunch, tea and dinner (last orders 9.30pm). Closed Sun evening.
Average Prices: A la Carte £8; Sun lunch £7.50; snacks from 70p.

The Bell and Bear is situated near to the lakes and watermeadows of Emberton Country Park. It is a pub built of mellow stone, with an aviary and children's play area in its pleasant garden to the rear. Wholesome snacks such as steak and kidney pie and real ales are available from the bar, whilst the restaurant sees a full à la carte menu. Here dishes include chicken chasseur and a range of steaks. Pensioner's dinner every Wednesday.

BELL & BEAR

12 High Street
Emberton Nr. Olney
Tel: 0234 711565

MILTON KEYNES TANDOORI RESTAURANT

141 Queensway (Market Place), Bletchley, Milton Keynes.
Tel: (0908) 75209/75692
Hours: Open for lunch and dinner (last orders 11.30pm).
Average Prices: A la Carte £10; wine £4.95 per litre.

A chef with over 20 years' experience is in charge of this family-owned business that offers a high standard of service and cuisine in intimate surroundings. Traditional tandoori based dishes are served and children are charged only half price. There is also a 10% discount on take-aways.

Milton Keynes Tandoori
RESTAURANT
(Fully Licensed)

141 Queensway
(Market Place)
Bletchley, Milton Keynes
0908 - 75209/75692

LAL BAGH RESTAURANT

Fenny Stratford, Bletchley, Milton Keynes.
Tel: (0908) 271494
Hours: Open for lunch and dinner (last orders 11.30pm).
Average Prices: A la Carte £10; wine £5.50 per bottle.

Unlike many Indian restaurants, Lal Bagh has a very modern, understated décor, with cane furnishings and a selection of Indian prints along the walls. The menu, however, is traditional and includes dishes such as lamb pasanda, khroi chicken and murgh makani. There is a 10% discount on takeaways.

Lal Bagh
RESTAURANT

47 Aylesbury Street
Fenny Stratford
0908 271494/644700

Buckinghamshire

THE LOWNDES ARMS AND HOTEL
4 High Street, Whaddon, Milton Keynes.
Tel: (0908) 501706
Hours: *Open for lunch and dinner (last orders 9.30pm).*
Closed Sun. Bar meals, except Sun.
Average Prices: *Bar meals 85p-£12.*
Wines: *House wine £5.50 per bottle.*

The village of Whaddon sits on the top of a plateau, overlooking wide open countryside that once formed part of the great royal hunting grounds of Whaddon Chase, first granted by Henry III. During the summer months there are few better spots to enjoy the view than in the gardens of The Lowndes Arms, whilst, in the winter, the bar itself is equally appealing with its inglenook fire stacked with logs, and oak beaming that dates the inn to the 1550's. The inn serves traditional pub cooking, but its speciality is rump steak in any size from 8-24 oz, served with onion rings, mushrooms and tomatoes. There are also dishes such as seafood platter, a 1½ lb roast chicken and 8 oz gammon steak. The accompanying house wine is Californian. For guests wishing to stay overnight the hotel provides ten en suite rooms with modern amenities which range from direct dial telephones to satellite TV. Visa, Access and Diner's cards are all accepted by hosts John and Rita Mony. The village can be found off the A5, south of Stony Stratford.

Lowndes Arms
4 High Street, Whaddon,
Milton Keynes. Tel: (0908) 501706

Buckinghamshire

THE BELL INN
Main Street, Beachampton.
Tel: (0908) 563861
Hours: Open for lunch and dinner (last orders 10pm).
Bar meals, except Sun evening.
Average Prices: A la Carte £13; Sun lunch £6.50; snacks from £2.25.
Wines: House wine £6.50 per bottle.

The ever encroaching outer boundaries of Milton Keynes have not yet stretched to the quiet country village of Beachampton. Its Bell Inn dates in part to the 17th century and has traditional oak beaming inside and a three-acre garden that is popular in the summer. Real ales are served from the bar along with numerous dishes which include all the pub favourites and some Italian specialities, reflecting the native country of the chef. Cannelloni, fettuccine and lasagne feature alongside steak and kidney pie, char-grills and curry. The main à la carte selection is also traditionally weighted with, for example as starters, smoked trout, seafood cocktail and garlic mushrooms. For the main course there is usually a choice between three fish dishes, such as salmon in a lobster sauce, plaice or swordfish, and veal, chicken and steak dishes. A dessert trolley, which changes daily, concludes. Sunday sees the traditional Sunday lunch, for which it is advisable to book early, and a special lunch for children. Low alcohol drinks feature prominently.

Main Street, Beachampton Tel: 0908 563861

**BEKASH
TANDOORI
INDIAN
RESTAURANT**

50 High Street
Stony Stratford
Milton Keynes

Tel: 0908
562249/568521

THE BEKASH TANDOORI
50 High Street, Stony Stratford.
Tel: (0908) 568521/562249
Hours: Open for lunch and dinner (last orders 11.15pm).
Average Prices: A la Carte £13.
Wines: House wine £5.50 per bottle.

Since its opening eight and a half years ago, The Bekash Tandoori has established a strong local reputation for the quality of its food and the standards of its service. A bar with a dark oak counter and comfortable armchairs greets diners entering the restaurant and is a welcome prelude to the meal. The main restaurant area is divided into two separate rooms, and the atmosphere is one of privacy, with numerous quiet corners conjured by polished oak divides.

The menu ranges over many Indian specialities, highlighting the versatility of the country's cuisine, with a knowledge of herbs and spices, and of their blending with various meats, vegetables and fish, well to the fore.

To begin a meal at The Bekash try appetisers such as king prawn butterfly (delicately spiced king prawns in ghee butter), prawn puri (fried spiced prawns with deep-fried unleavened bread), or, perhaps, lamb or chicken tikka.

Traditionally the main course should consist of three dishes, a main dish, a side dish and a staple dish which usually consists of bread such as nan or chapati. The choice of main course dish is wide with, for example, tandooris, mild to hot curries, Persian dishes, biriani dishes and house specialities. Typical of the selection is tandoori king prawn (flavoured with various special spices and cooked with onions, capsicum and tomatoes), lamb pasanda, chicken tikka masala, chicken dopiaza, and chicken dhansak (a Persian dish which is both sweet, sour and hot, cooked with delicate spices and lentils and served with pilau rice). From the selection of curries, try meat Kashmiri with lychee (mild), rogon ghosht (garnished with tomatoes and onion, medium), or chicken sylhet (extremely hot).

Those who have difficulty choosing from the sometimes bewildering selections could opt for one of the set meals (for two, three or four persons). There is also a special kurzi lamb or chicken feast which requires 24 hours' notice on account of the long time needed for the marinade. Parties are also catered for.

Whilst we believe that all factual details are correct, we suggest that readers check, when making reservations, that prices and other facts quoted meet their requirements.

Buckinghamshire

THE OLNEY WINE BAR

9 High Street South, Olney. Tel: (0234) 711112
Hours: Open for lunch and dinner (last orders 10pm, 10.30pm Sat). Open Sun lunch, closed Sun evening.
Average Prices: A la Carte £7; snacks from £1.50.
Wines: House wine £4.30 per carafe; £5.30 per bottle.

Situated on the River Ouse, Olney is a market town famous for its pancake race annually run down the High Street for the last 500 years. The Georgian and bow-fronted wine bar leads directly off the High Street and was once a bakery. Some of the old ovens can still be seen in the bar area which serves bistro-style fare. Prawns in garlic butter, corn on the cob, taramasalata with pitta bread and seafood cocktail can all be found on the list of starters. Main courses feature quiches, pies, cold meats, steaks and dishes such as lasagne and moussaka. Run by Roy Plumbridge and his son, Nick, the premises actually feature three restaurants, with the main menu chalked up on a blackboard. House specialities begin with prawn pilpil, followed by Swedish chicken (served with apples, raisins, bananas and almonds in a curry-flavoured mayonnaise) and desserts such as Westmorland tart (mixed fruits and nuts with rum and rum-flavoured cream on a biscuit base), cherry and hazelnut roulade or cheesecake. Children and vegetarians are both catered for and the wine list spans 50 popular European labels.

The
Olney Wine Bar

FOR GOOD FOOD AND WINE

9 High Street South, Olney,
Buckinghamshire
Tel: BEDFORD (0234) 711112
For Enquiries and Reservations

THE SWAN REVIVED HOTEL

High Street, Newport Pagnell. Tel: (0908) 610565
Hours: Open for coffee, lunch, tea and dinner (last orders 10pm). Bar meals evenings, except Sun.
Average Prices: A la Carte £11; Sun lunch £7.25.
Wines: House wine £5.50 per bottle.

Built in 1681 with a typically Georgian facade, The Swan stands in the very heart of Newport Pagnell. Conferences and private parties are catered for in the Sherington and Stafford rooms, whilst there is accommodation in 40 en suite bedrooms with two executive suites. The dining room is traditional both in its style of cooking and furnishings. Dark oak panelling and tables are matched by leather upholstered chairs with brass studding, all reminiscent of the Tudor age. Fresh flowers add sparkle. The menu covers fish, grills, poultry, entrées, vegetarian dishes and chef's specialities. Begin, perhaps, with honey dew melon fan and raspberry sorbet, or Mediterranean king prawns in garlic butter. Moving onto the main course, there is poached Scottish salmon steak with a hollandaise sauce, breast of chicken with a cream and Pernod sauce and lamb cutlets served on a bed of spinach with a redcurrant sauce. Vegetarian diners see nut roast with a tomato, onion and garlic sauce. Speciality coffees conclude.

HIGH ST.
NEWPORT PAGNELL,
BUCKS. MK16 8AR

TEL: (0908) 610565
TELEX: 826801

Buckinghamshire/Bedfordshire

GLOVERS RESTAURANT
St John Street, Newport Pagnell. Tel: (0908) 616398
Hours: Open for lunch and dinner. Closed Sun/Mon.
Average Prices: Set price £19.50; 10% discount lunchtime food.

Just ten minutes from Milton Keynes centre and five minutes from M1 junction 14, Glovers offers gracious old world charm in a late 17th century building, with its welcoming, tranquil combination of beams, stone walls and inglenooks, warmed by a real log fire. Friendly but unobtrusive service complements a seasonal menu which offers excitingly different combinations of fresh foods, herbs and sauces. Established 15 years; chef-patron.

GLOVERS

18-20 St John Street
Newport Pagnell, Bucks MK16 9HJ
Tel: 0908 616598

SORRENTINO RESTAURANT
Ram Yard, Bedford. Tel: (0234) 50755
Hours: Open for lunch and dinner, except Sun (last orders 11pm).
Average Prices: A la Carte £13; Table d'Hôte £7.85.

Chef-proprietor Alfredo Sorrentino has created a menu illustrating the varied regional cuisines of Italy which range from simple, but tasty pasta dishes to the more sophisticated combinations of filetto Sorrentino (beef in mushrooms and wine) and trota con mandorli (trout in almonds and cream). The atmosphere of the restaurant in turn reflects the homely style of the cookery.

SORRENTINO
RESTAURANT

High Street, Ram Yard
Bedford Tel: (0234) 50755

THE BEDFORD ARMS HOTEL
George Street, Woburn.
Tel: (0525) 290441 Fax: (0525) 290432
Hours: Open for coffee, lunch, tea and dinner. Bar meals.
Average Prices: A la Carte £18; Table d'Hôte £13; snacks from £3.
Wines: House wine £6.95 per bottle.

The village of Woburn once formed part of the estate of the Dukes of Bedford who lived at nearby Woburn Abbey and, after a serious fire gutted the village in 1724, the family rebuilt it along Georgian lines. Their architect, Henry Holland, re-designed the inn whose restaurant now takes his name. The Bedford Arms has been fully modernised and today offers 55 fully equipped bedrooms, a Tavern Bar (which retains some of the heavy beaming from the original Medieval inn) and Holland's Restaurant, with its adjoining cocktail bar. Dishes are generally French in origin and there is a selection of hot and cold hors d'oeuvre which include Camembert à la frites (deep-fried with a bed of crispy salad and garlic mayonnaise) and melon celeste (ogen melon boat with a cargo of exotic fruits). Main courses cover fish, meat, grills and dishes cooked at the table, like suprême de volaille Marquis (breast of chicken flamed in a sherry and paprika sauce with prawns and smoked salmon) and scampi Martini (tossed in vermouth and butter and finished in a cream sauce of mushrooms and dill on a bed of green noodles). Business meetings and conferences catered for.

THE BEDFORD ARMS HOTEL

GEORGE STREET,
WOBURN,
MILTON KEYNES

TEL: (0525) 290441
FAX: (0525) 290432
TELEX: 825205

Bedfordshire

PARIS HOUSE RESTAURANT
Woburn Park, Woburn.
Tel: (0525) 290692
Hours: *Open for lunch and dinner (last orders 9.30pm).*
Closed Sun evening and Mon.
Average Prices: *Table d'Hôte £23; Sun lunch £18.50.*
Wines: *House wine £8 per bottle.*

Peter Chandler, the award-winning chef at Paris House, also features in the Chef's Choice at the front of this guide. The success of a restaurant depends on its setting as well as its chef and Paris House can be found situated in a Victorian folly built for the Paris exhibition of 1878 and brought back to the abbey's grounds by the 6th Duke of Bedford. Inside, the rich décor underscores the style of Peter's cooking which closely resembles that of the Roux brothers, with whom he previously worked. Begin a meal with a salad of potted duck, or monkfish with noodles in a creamy bacon, onion and mushroom sauce. For the main course there may be guinea fowl with a brandy and cream sauce, a medley of fish in two sauces, chicken basquaise (from the Basque region, with a pepper and wine sauce and served with a side salad of chicory and fresh beans), or rack of saffron lamb. Desserts show a light touch and feature raspberry soufflé and some delicate pastry work.

Paris House

Woburn
Tel: 0525 290692

Bedfordshire

THE BELL INN
21 Bedford Street, Woburn. Tel: (0525) 290280
Hours: Open for coffee, lunch and dinner. Bar meals 7 days.
Average Prices: A la Carte £20; Table d'Hôte £15.95; snacks from £2.25.

The Bell Inn and Hotel face each other across the road, offering both accommodation and dining in traditional countrified surroundings. The main restaurant is framed with beams and its creamy walls and peach décor make a warm accompaniment to a menu which combines nouvelle and traditional dishes. More modest meals are chalked up on a blackboard in the bar, where Greene King ales are also available.

THE COCK HORSE
Heath and Reach, near Leighton Buzzard.
Tel: (052 523) 7816
Hours: Open for coffee, lunch and dinner (last orders 9.45pm).
Average Prices: A la Carte £16; Sun lunch £10.50; snacks from £1.50.

The Cock Horse stands just off the main A5. It has recently opened a new restaurant which serves an interesting menu beginning with dishes such as a Wiltshire purse (prawns and smoked trout parcel set on a bed of salad leaves) and followed by pan-fried calves' liver with an apple and sherry gravy. Sweets are from the trolley and there are real ales from the bar. Accommodation too.

Bedfordshire

THE CARPENTERS ARMS

Sundon Road, Harlington. Tel: (052 55) 2384
Hours: Open for lunch and dinner (last orders 9.15pm).
                Closed Sun/Mon/Tues evenings. Bar meals.
Average Prices: A la Carte £13.50; Sun lunch £7.95; business lunch £7.95.

One mile from junction 12 of the M1, The Carpenters Arms is a restored, listed 17th century building serving traditional ales (Webster's, Ruddles and more) and with a restaurant decorated to a cottagey style. Home cooking dominates and most ingredients are locally supplied. Ice cream desserts are home-made. Business lunches are very popular.

The Carpenters Arms
Harlington

À La Carte Restaurant
Home Cooked Hot & Cold Bar Meals

Sundon Road, Harlington
Tel: (05255) 2384

THE RED LION

Market Square, Toddington. Tel: (052 55) 2524
Hours: Open for lunch and dinner (last orders 9.45pm).
                Closed Sun/Mon evening.
Average Prices: A la Carte £14.50; Sun lunch £6.50 (3 course);
                snacks from £1.75.

The Red Lion is a 400-year-old pub situated overlooking the village green and supposedly haunted by a friendly lady ghost. Its 32-seater restaurant serves a menu of attractively presented dishes such as carpet bag tournedos (fillet steak stuffed with oysters), châteaubriand (for two) and homard thermidor (lobster picked from a tank).

Red Lion
Restaurant

Market Square, Toddington
Tel: (052 55) 2524

THE CHILTERN CREST HOTEL
Waller Avenue, off Dunstable Road, Luton.
Tel: (0582) 575911

Hours: Open for coffee, lunch and dinner (last orders 9.45pm).
Average Prices: A la Carte £17.50; Table d'Hôte from £11.45; Sun lunch from £9.45; snacks from £1.50.
Wines: House wine £7.95 per bottle.

The Chiltern Crest Hotel at Luton, like others in this nationwide group, is both modern and comfortable. Situated one mile from junction 11 of the M1 and close to the centre of Luton, it is also a convenient base for business meetings and other functions. Accommodation is provided in 94 rooms and there are ample conference facilities. Diners at Pinkerton's Restaurant are offered a choice of menus, ranging from the traditional à la carte selection to separate menus for children, diabetics and vegetarians. At the weekend there is a special fixed price menu with a choice of five dishes per course. Typical of the selection of starters from the main menu are smoked salmon, wild mushrooms, avocado and port in melon. The main course covers fish, meat and poultry with, for example, Dover sole, peppered steak and chicken breast in an orange and Grand Marnier sauce. Sunday lunch is also very popular, particularly with families. All the leading credit cards are accepted. Menu dishes may change with the new à la carte.

CHILTERN CREST HOTEL
LUTON

WALLER AVENUE, DUNSTABLE ROAD, LUTON. TEL: (0582) 575911

Bedfordshire

RISTORANTE CASA BIANCA

26 Chapel Street, Luton. Tel: (0582) 27916
Hours: Open for lunch and dinner (last orders 11pm, Dine and Dance Restaurant 2am). Closed Sun.
Average Prices: A la Carte £13.50.
Wines: House wine £7 per bottle.

Amidst the hustle and bustle of Luton's busy town centre, the Casa Bianca offers a welcome retreat in which to enjoy a taste of authentic Italy. Under one roof are three different styles of atmosphere and cuisine to suit a variety of moods. The first floor houses an attractive dine and dance restaurant which offers a first class à la carte selection. There is a choice of party menus as well and, since it is open until late, it makes an ideal venue for a whole range of functions. On the ground floor is Vinos trattoria, whose varied menu consists of pizzas, pastas, steaks, fish, chicken dishes and salads. The informal atmosphere at lunchtime changes in the evening when candles and linen cloths covering the tables induce a more romantic ambience. There is also a wine bar with hanging plants and marble tables which give it the air of a piazza. The atmosphere here is lively and bright and is a popular spot for lunchtime snacks. Major credit cards are accepted.

RISTORANTE CASA BIANCA 26 Chapel Street, Luton Tel: 0582 27916

Bedfordshire

STRATHMORE THISTLE HOTEL
Arndale Centre, Luton. Tel: (0582) 34199
Hours: Open for coffee, lunch, tea and dinner (last orders 9.50pm).
Average Prices: A la Carte £18; Table d'Hôte £16; Sun lunch £12.50.
Wines: House wine £7.35.

The Strathmore Thistle, an attractive modern hotel, is situated in the heart of Luton. The entrance foyer immediately impresses with its pillars and marbled floor, and the hallmarks of the interior are quality furnishings and a spacious elegant atmosphere. Angelines Restaurant, decorated in a pastel peach and beige, has a stylish ambience which complements its Continental menu. Starters reveal ogen melon with prawns, Stilton mushrooms and chef's pâté, encased in a pastry case and covered in a warm Napoleon liqueur sauce. For the main course there is scampi Miracle (Dublin Bay scampi wrapped in bacon with a hot tomato sauce), veal escalope and scampi with vermouth, and supreme of chicken with a smoked cheese sauce. Sweets are from the trolley. Alternatively, there are snacks from Mr Bumble's Bar, or the informal Balzac's Bistro, decorated in oak and with a scattering of pot plants. Their bistro fare includes chicken Kiev, spaghetti bolognaise, stuffed jacket potatoes and steaks. Extensive conference facilities, with up to 250 catered for, are available in the Windsor Suite.

Strathmore Thistle Hotel, Arndale Centre, Luton. Tel: 0582 34199

Bedfordshire

HOTEL IBIS
Luton International Airport, Spittlesea Road, Luton.
Tel: (0582) 424488. Temporary Number: (0582) 391627
Hours: Open for breakfast (from 6.30am), coffee, lunch, tea and dinner (last orders 10.30pm).
Average Prices: A la Carte £10; Sun lunch £8.50; snacks from £2.
Wines: House wine £6.90 per bottle.

Hotel Ibis, part of a large international group, is Luton Airport's first and only hotel. It caters for a wide variety of functions from simply providing accommodation in one of 98 bedrooms, to the more elaborate conference facilities. The restaurant looks out onto the continuous stream of air traffic and has a pleasant pastel décor. The menu is internationally geared, incorporating grill dishes, a range of daily specials and a self-service salad buffet. For a starter there is a choice between appetisers like ham and cheese croissant or Ardennes pâté. Main course dishes include rib steak of beef, supreme of chicken tarragon and scaloppine of pork napolitaine. The selection of desserts includes tempting offerings such as hot red fruits on ice cream. All the major credit cards are accepted.

Hotel Ibis, Spittlesea Road, Luton International Airport. Tel: 0582 424488

Bedfordshire

THE WHITE HORSE
1 Market Square, Eaton Bray. Tel: (0525) 220231
Hours: *Open for coffee, lunch and dinner (last orders 9.15pm). Closed Sun evening/Mon.*
Average Prices: *A la Carte £15; Sun lunch £7.50; snacks from £1.20.*
Wines: *House wine £5.25 per bottle.*

The White Horse has overlooked the village green of Eaton Bray for the last 200 years and has a pleasant exterior and a homely interior filled with brass ornaments and fresh flowers. The restaurant is candlelit, serving a French and traditional menu with ample choice. Start with melon framboise (half ogen melon filled with a raspberry purée laced with liqueur), or escargots flambéed in Pernod. The main course sees fish dishes, with shark steak in asparagus sauce; vegetarian dishes, with vegetable and nut vol au vents in a rich mushroom sauce, and traditional meat dishes which include medallions of beef Madeira, home-made pigeon pie and pork fillet applejack (medallions of pork sautéed in a calvados sauce). Desserts feature a fresh pineapple platter served with a dark or milk chocolate dip, Eve's pudding (baked apples with a sponge topping) and the 'sparrow's nest' (light meringue filled with whipped cream and topped with fresh seasonal fruit). The wine list intermingles popular labels with some quality lesser known international wines. There is also a wide selection of bar meals and real ale.

The White Horse
Eaton Bray Tel: (0525) 220231

Bedfordshire

Queen's Head Hotel
2 Rushden Road, Milton Ernest
Tel: 0234 272822

Miller's
RESTAURANT

Where can you find superb cuisine and excellent wines within a beautiful setting?
At Miller's, the restaurant at the new Queens Head Hotel, Milton Ernest.
Open to non residents seven days a week.

THE QUEENS HEAD
HOTEL & RESTAURANT

On the A6 five miles North of Bedford. Telephone 0234-272822

Bedfordshire

THE QUEEN'S HEAD HOTEL
2 Rushden Road, Milton Ernest.
Tel: (0234) 272822   Fax: (023 02) 2337.
Hours: Open for breakfast, 7.30-10am, coffee, 7.30am-2.30pm, lunch, 12-2pm, and dinner, 7-10pm, every day. Bar meals 12-2pm and 7-10pm.
Average Prices: A la Carte from £14; Sun lunch from £10; bar meals from £2.50.
Wines: From £5 per bottle.

The village of Milton Ernest is situated just off the A6, six miles north of the county town of Bedford. The Queen's Head is owned by the well-known local brewing group Charles Wells, which has developed it from a simple 17th century inn into a modern hotel, retaining its olde-world charm and its 17th century character.

Accommodation is provided not only in a modern extension, which blends with the character of the existing building, but also in a splendid barn conversion. The dominant colours are pink and beige, with each room individually named after a character from the village's past. The Susannah Rolt Room, for example, recalls a 17th century benefactress who bequeathed loaves of bread to be distributed to the poor each Sunday.

An appreciation of the 17th century is also retained in the atmosphere of the two bars, a cosy snug bar and a lounge bar area, and in Miller's Restaurant. This is named after Glen Miller, who was stationed nearby during World War II and was a frequent visitor to the inn. Low beaming, contrasting pink and white napery and Victorian glass candles characterize the décor, giving the room a soft atmosphere for evening dining.

The menu is traditional with a Continental flavour, offering fine dishes from around the world and beginning with appetisers such as tropical fruit salad, garlic prawns, cheese dumplings and oriental ribs. For a main course dish try the rack of English lamb with honey and apricots, or halibut steak with prawns and mushrooms in a creamy sauce. And, to conclude, there is a selection of desserts which includes fresh kiwi and pineapple Pavlova, banoffi pie and profiteroles in a chocolate sauce. The wine list presents a selection of 64 wines, including half-bottles.

Bar meals are available and these feature stuffed jacket potatoes with salad, Portuguese sardines cooked in garlic, or perhaps vegetable chilli with a side salad and garlic bread. Accompanying real ales are the Charles Wells stalwarts Eagle and Bombardier from the award-winning cellar, along with the popular cosmopolitan lager Red Stripe. Licensing hours are 11-3pm and 5.30-11pm, Monday to Saturday, and 12-2.30pm and 7-10pm on Sunday, although visitors should check any variation at Bank Holidays.

Glossary

To assist readers in making the sometimes confusing choice from the menu, we have listed some of the most popular dishes from restaurants featured in *Where to Eat* up and down the country, together with a brief, general explanation of each item. Of course, this can never be a comprehensive listing — regional trends result in variation in the preparation of each dish, and there's no accounting for the flair and versatility of the chef — but we hope it offers readers a useful guideline to those enigmatic menu items.

STARTERS

Foie gras .... duck or goose liver, often made into pâté
Gazpacho .... a chilled Spanish soup of onion, tomato, pepper and cucumber
Gravad lax .... raw salmon marinated in dill, pepper, salt and sugar
Guacamole .... a creamy paste of avocado flavoured with coriander and garlic
Hummus ..... a tangy paste of crushed chick peas flavoured with garlic and lemon
Meze .... a variety of spiced Greek hors d'oeuvre
Moules marinière .... mussels in a sauce of white wine and onions
Samosa .... small pastry parcels of spiced meat or vegetables
Satay .... small skewers of grilled meat served with a spicy peanut dip
Taramasalata .... a creamy, pink paste of fish roe
Tzatziki .... yoghurt with cucumber and garlic
Vichyssoise .... a thick, creamy leek and potato soup, served cold

FISH

Bouillabaisse .... chunky fish stew from the south of France

Coquilles St Jacques .... scallops
Lobster Newburg .... with cream, stock and, sometimes, sherry
Lobster thermidor .... served in the shell with a cream and mustard sauce, glazed in the oven
Sole Walewska .... a rich dish of poached fish in a Mornay sauce with lobster
Sole bonne femme .... cooked with stock, dry white wine, parsley and butter
Sole véronique .... poached in a wine sauce with grapes
Trout meunière .... floured, fried and topped with butter, parsley and lemon

MAIN COURSES

Beef Stroganoff .... strips of fillet steak sautéed and served in a sauce of wine and cream
Beef Wellington .... beef in a pastry crust
Boeuf Bourguignon .... steak braised in a red wine sauce with onions, bacon and mushrooms
Chateaubriand .... thick slice of very tender fillet steak
Chicken à la King .... pieces of chicken in a creamy sauce
Chicken Kiev .... crumbed breast filled with herb butter, often garlic
Chicken Marengo .... with tomato, white wine and garlic
Chicken Maryland ..... fried and served with bacon, corn fritters and fried banana
Osso buco .... knuckle of veal cooked with white wine, tomato and onion
Pork Normandy .... with cider, cream and calvados
Ris de veau .... calves' sweetbreads
Saltimbocca alla romana .... veal topped with ham, cooked with sage and white wine

Steak au poivre .... steak in a pepper and wine sauce
Steak bordelaise .... steak in a red wine sauce with bone marrow
Steak Diane .... steak in a peppered, creamy sauce
Steak tartare .... raw, minced steak served with egg yolk
Tournedos Rossini ...... fillet steak on a croûton, topped with foie gras and truffles
Wiener Schnitzel .... escalope of veal, breadcrumbed and fried

SAUCES

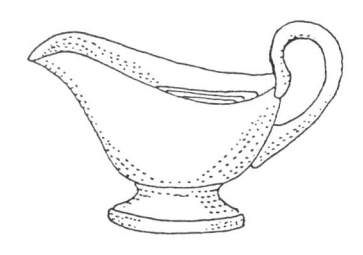

Aioli .... strong garlic mayonnaise
Anglaise .... thick white sauce of stock mixed with egg yolks, lemon and pepper
Arrabbiata .... tomatoes, garlic and hot peppers
Béarnaise .... thick sauce of egg yolks, vinegar, shallots, white wine and butter
Carbonara .... bacon, egg and Parmesan cheese
Chasseur .... mushrooms, tomatoes, shallots and white wine
Dijonnaise .... cold sauce of eggs and mustard, similar to mayonnaise
Hollandaise .... egg yolks and clarified butter
Mornay .... creamy sauce of milk and egg yolks flavoured with Gruyère cheese
Pesto .... basil, marjoram, parsley, garlic, oil and Parmesan cheese
Pizzaiola .... tomatoes, herbs, garlic and pepper
Provençale .... tomato, garlic, onion and white wine
Reform .... pepper and white wine with boiled egg whites, gherkins and mushrooms
Rémoulade .... mayonnaise with mustard, capers, gherkins and herbs, served cold

DESSERTS

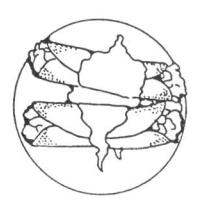

Banoffi pie .... with toffee and banana
Bavarois .... cold custard with whipped cream and, usually, fruit
Crème brûlée .... caramel-topped, rich vanilla flavoured cream
Crêpes Suzette .... pancakes flavoured with orange or tangerine liqueur
Parfait .... chilled dessert with fresh cream
Pavé .... square shaped light sponge
Pavlova .... meringue-based fruit dessert
Sabayon/zabaglione .... whisked egg yolks, wine and sugar
Syllabub .... whipped cream, wine and sherry
Zuccotto .... a dome of liqueur-soaked sponge filled with fruit and cream
Zuppa inglese .... an Italian trifle

CULINARY TERMS

Coulis .... a thin purée of cooked vegetables or fruit
Croustade .... a case of pastry, bread or baked potato which can be filled
Devilled .... seasoned and spicy, often with mustard or cayenne
Dim-sum .... various Chinese savoury pastries and dumplings
Duxelles .... stuffing of chopped mushrooms and shallots
En croûte .... in a pastry or bread case
Farce .... a delicate stuffing
Feuilleté .... filled slice of puff pastry
Florentine .... containing spinach
Goujons .... thin strips of fish
Julienne .... cut into thin slices
Magret .... a cut from the breast of a duck
Mille-feuille .... thin layers of filled puff pastry
Quenelles .... spiced fish or meat balls
Roulade .... stuffed and rolled
Sauté .... to brown in oil
Tournedos .... small slice of thick fillet

Index

ALPHABETICAL INDEX TO ESTABLISHMENTS

The Aristocrat, Aylesbury 32
B's Restaurant, Stoke Mandeville 34
Barnaby's Carvery, Loughton, Milton Keynes 54
The Bedford Arms Hotel, Woburn 69
The Bekash Tandoori, Stony Stratford 65
The Bell and Bear, Emberton, near Olney 60
The Bell Inn, Aston Clinton 50
The Bell Inn, Beachampton 63
The Bell Inn, Woburn 71
The Bell Inn and Motel, Codicote, Hitchin 27
The Bernard Arms Hotel, Great Kimble, near Aylesbury 39
The Blue Flag, Cadmore End, High Wycombe 41
The Boot, Soulbury, near Leighton Buzzard 35
The Broughton Hotel, Broughton Village, Milton Keynes 55
The Bull Hotel, Gerrards Cross 45
Calendars Café Bar and Restaurant, Garston, Watford 31
The Carpenters Arms, Harlington 72
The Casanova Restaurant, Hertford 23
Chequers Inn, Hotel and Restaurant, Wooburn Common 43
The Chiltern Crest Hotel, Luton 73
Claridges, Bovingdon 28
Claudius Italian Restaurant, St Albans 16
The Cock Horse, Heath and Reach, near Leighton Buzzard 71
The Comet Hotel, Hatfield 18
The Compleat Angler Hotel, Marlow 42
Dean Park Hotel, Watford 32
Dipalee Tandoori, Buckingham 53
The Edgwarebury Hotel, Elstree 19
The Galleria Bar Brasserie, Berkhamsted 29
The George and Dragon, Watton-at-Stone 22
Glovers Restaurant, Newport Pagnell 68
The Golden Lion, London Colney, St Albans 17
Gusty's Carvery at The King's Arms, Berkhamsted 28
The Halfway House, Wendover Dene 36
Harpenden Moat House, Harpenden 17
Hartwell House, Hartwell, Aylesbury 33
The Hit or Miss Inn, Penn Street Village, near Amersham 43
Hotel Ibis, Luton 76
Houstons Restaurant, Milton Keynes 58
Jade Garden, St Albans 14

Jaipur Restaurant, Milton Keynes	57
King William IV, Speen, near Aylesbury	37
Lal Bagh Restaurant, Fenny Stratford, Bletchley, Milton Keynes	61
La Province Restaurant, St Albans	15
Le Garde Manger, Letchworth	24
The Lowndes Arms and Hotel, Whaddon, Milton Keynes	62
Milton Keynes Tandoori Restaurant, Bletchley, Milton Keynes	61
The Old Barge, Hertford	24
The Old Bull Inn, Royston	25
The Old Plow Inn and Restaurant, Flowers Bottom, Speen, near High Wycombe	38
The Old Swan, Cheddington, near Leighton Buzzard	35
The Old Thatched Inn and Restaurant, Adstock	51
The Olney Wine Bar, Olney	66
Padrini, Aylesbury	34
Paris House Restaurant, Woburn	70
The Penny Farthing Restaurant, Berkhamsted	30
The Pheasant Inn, Ballinger Common, near Great Missenden	37
The Post House Hotel, Milton Keynes	59
Queen Adelaide Public House, Shenley	18
The Queen's Head Hotel, Milton Ernest	79
Redcoats Farmhouse Hotel, Redcoats Green, near Hitchin	26
The Red Lion, Toddington	72
Ristorante Casa Bianca, Luton	74
Robin Hood Public House and Restaurant, Ridgeway, Botany Bay, near Enfield	21
The Rose and Crown Inn and Restaurant, Saunderton, near Princes Risborough	40
The Royal Standard of England, Forty Green, Beaconsfield	47
St Michael's Manor Hotel, St Albans	13
The Shelswell Inn, Newton Purcell	49
Simpson's Brasserie, Princes Risborough	39
Sopwell House, Sopwell, St Albans	16
Sorrentino Restaurant, Bedford	68
Strathmore Thistle Hotel, Luton	75
The Swan Revived Hotel, Newport Pagnell	67
Torenzo Italian Restaurant and Pizzeria, Milton Keynes	60
The Villiers Hotel, Buckingham	52
West Lodge Park, Hadley Wood, near Barnet	20
Wheelers of Beaconsfield, Beaconsfield	48
The White Horse, Eaton Bray	77
Woughton House Hotel, Woughton-on-the-Green, Milton Keynes	56

ALPHABETICAL INDEX TO TOWNS AND VILLAGES

HERTFORDSHIRE

Barnet 20
Berkhamsted 28
Botany Bay 21
Bovingdon 28
Codicote 27
Elstree 19
Enfield 21
Garston 31
Hadley Wood 20
Harpenden 17
Hatfield 18
Hertford 23
Hitchin 26
Letchworth 24
London Colney 17
Redcoats Green 26
Ridgeway 21
Royston 25
St Albans 13
Shenley 18
Sopwell 16
Watford 31
Watton-at-Stone 22

BUCKINGHAMSHIRE

Adstock 51
Amersham 43
Aston Clinton 50
Aylesbury 32
Ballinger Common 37
Beachampton 63
Beaconsfield 47
Bletchley 61
Broughton Village 55
Buckingham 52
Cadmore End 41

Cheddington 35
Emberton 60
Fenny Stratford 61
Flowers Bottom 38
Forty Green 47
Gerrards Cross 45
Great Kimble 39
Great Missenden 37
Hartwell 33
High Wycombe 41
Loughton 54
Marlow 42
Milton Keynes 54
Newport Pagnell 67
Newton Purcell 49
Olney 66
Penn Street Village 43
Princes Risborough 39
Saunderton 40
Soulbury 35
Speen 37
Stoke Mandeville 34
Stony Stratford 65
Wendover Dene 36
Whaddon 62
Wooburn Common 43
Woughton-on-the-Green 56

BEDFORDSHIRE

Bedford 68
Eaton Bray 77
Harlington 72
Heath and Reach 71
Leighton Buzzard 35, 71
Luton 73
Milton Ernest 79
Toddington 72
Woburn 69

*Peckish
in Perth?*

*Hungry
in Holyhead?*

*Famished
in Felixstowe?*

*Ravenous
in Roscommon?*

■ WHERE TO EAT ■

The discerning diner's guide
to restaurants throughout
Britain and Ireland

*Copies available from bookshops
or direct from the publishers*
Kingsclere Publications Ltd
Use the Order Form overleaf

ORDER FORM

To:
KINGSCLERE PUBLICATIONS LTD.
Highfield House, 2 Highfield Avenue, Newbury, Berkshire, RG14 5DS

Please send me
___ copies of *WHERE TO EAT in BERKSHIRE* @ £1.95   £ ___
___ copies of *WHERE TO EAT in BRISTOL, BATH & AVON* @ £2.50   £ ___
___ copies of *WHERE TO EAT in CORNWALL* @ £1.95   £ ___
___ copies of *WHERE TO EAT in CUMBRIA & THE LAKE DISTRICT* @ £1.95 £ ___
___ copies of *WHERE TO EAT in DORSET* @ £1.95   £ ___
___ copies of *WHERE TO EAT in EAST ANGLIA* @ £2.95   £ ___
___ copies of *WHERE TO EAT in EAST MIDLANDS* @ £1.95   £ ___
___ copies of *WHERE TO EAT in GLOS & THE COTSWOLDS* @ £1.95   £ ___
___ copies of *WHERE TO EAT in GUERNSEY* @ £0.80   £ ___
___ copies of *WHERE TO EAT in HAMPSHIRE* @ £1.95   £ ___
___ copies of *WHERE TO EAT in HERTS, BUCKS & BEDS* @ £2.50   £ ___
___ copies of *WHERE TO EAT in IRELAND* @ £1.75   £ ___
___ copies of *WHERE TO EAT in JERSEY* @ £0.80   £ ___
___ copies of *WHERE TO EAT in KENT* @ £2.95   £ ___
___ copies of *WHERE TO EAT in NORTH EAST ENGLAND* @ £1.95   £ ___
___ copies of *WHERE TO EAT in OXFORD & OXFORDSHIRE* @ £1.95   £ ___
___ copies of *WHERE TO EAT in SCOTLAND* @ £1.95   £ ___
___ copies of *WHERE TO EAT in SOMERSET* @ £1.95   £ ___
___ copies of *WHERE TO EAT in SURREY* @ £1.95   £ ___
___ copies of *WHERE TO EAT in SUSSEX* @ £2.95   £ ___
___ copies of *WHERE TO EAT in WALES* @ £2.95   £ ___
___ copies of *WHERE TO EAT in WILTSHIRE* @ £1.95   £ ___
___ copies of *WHERE TO EAT in YORKS & HUMBERSIDE* @ £1.95   £ ___
p&p at £0.50 (single copy), £1 (2-5 copies), £2 (6 copies)   £ ___
                                                  GRAND TOTAL   £ ___

Name ....

Address ....

....

Post code .... Cheque enclosed for £ ....

Your help in answering the following would be appreciated:
(1) Did you buy this guide at a SHOP ☐   TOURIST OFFICE ☐   GARAGE ☐   OTHER ☐
(2) Are any of your favourite eating places *not* listed in this guide? If so, could you please supply names and locations ....

....

....

(HBB.2)